D1247017

THE BLOSSOMING BOTANICAL GARDENS OF THE CHINESE ACADEMY OF SCIENCES

Honorary Editor-in-Chief   Wu Chengyih

Editor-in-Chief   Tong Fengqin

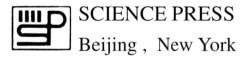

SCIENCE PRESS

Beijing , New York

1 9 9 7

Responsible Editors : Ma Suqing and Chai Yuting

Copyright © 1997 by Science Press
Published by Science Press
16 Donghuangchenggen North Street
Beijing 100717, China

Printed in Shenzhen

All rights reserved. No part of this publication may be repro-
duced, stored in a retrieval system, or transmitted in any
form or by any means, electronic, mechanical, photocopying,
recording or otherwise, without the prior written permission
of the copyright owners.

ISBN 7-03-006178-0/Q • 739

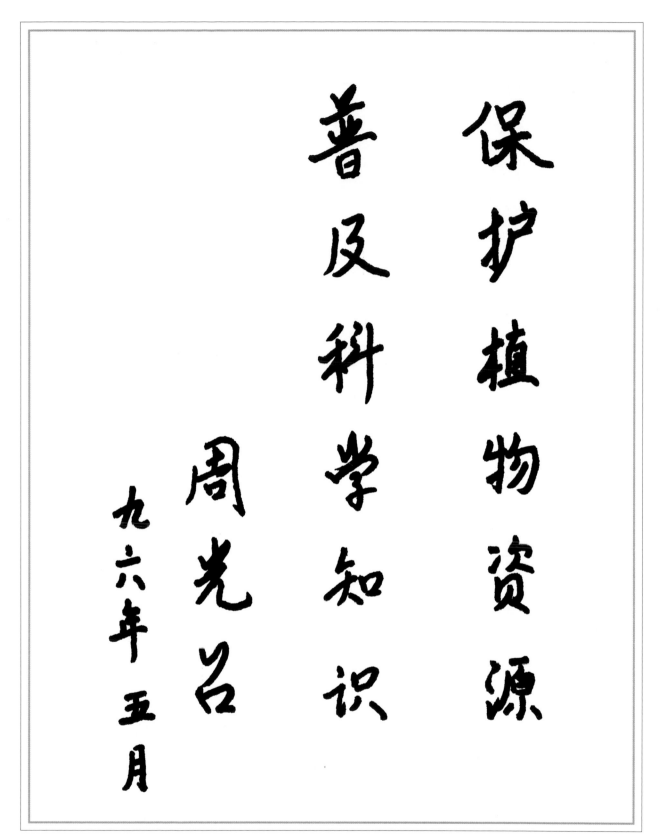

保护植物资源

普及科学知识

周光召

九六年五月

Conserve plant resources and spread scientific knowledge.

Zhou Guangzhao

May 1996

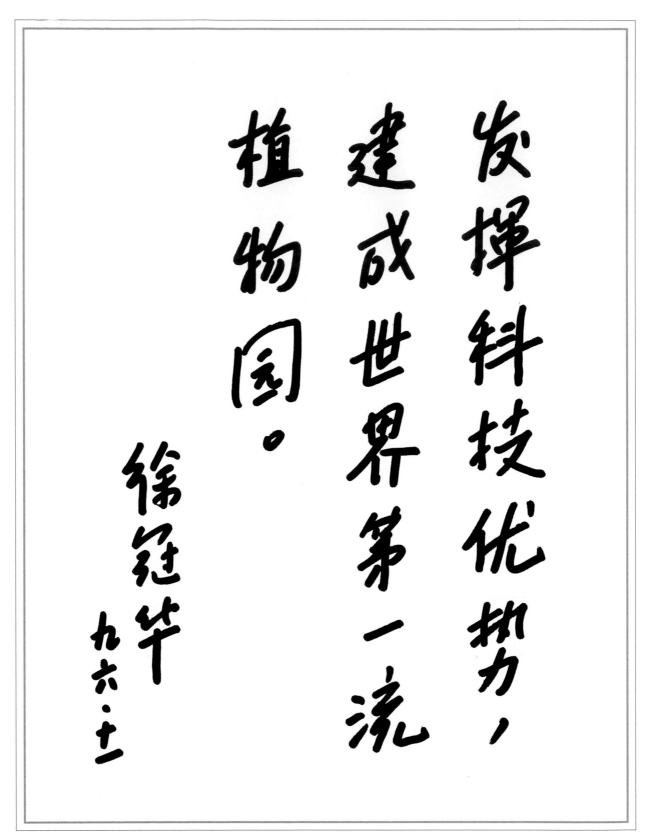

发挥科技优势，
建成世界第一流
植物园。

徐冠华
九六·十一

Make the most of the scientific and technological preponderance to build up world-class botanical gardens.

Xu Guanhua

November 1996

把植物园建设成为集科学研究、生物多样性保护和资源开发利用，以及植物科学知识普及教育为一体的重要基地。

许智宏
一九九七年三月

Construct the botanical gardens into important bases combining scientific research, conservation of biodiversity, development and utilization of resources, public education and popularization of knowledge of plant sciences.

Xu Zhihong

March 1996

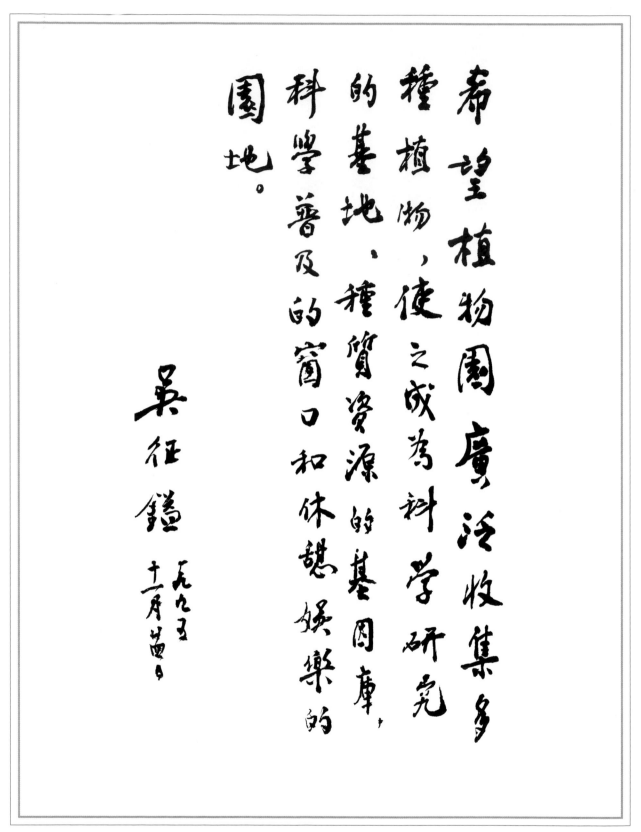

希望植物園廣泛收集多
種植物，使之成為科學研究
的基地，種質資源的基因庫，
科學普及的窗口和休憩娛樂的
園地。

吳征鎰 一九九五
十一月廿四日

I hope the botanical gardens develop comprehensive collections of wide ranges of plants to become bases for scientific research, gene banks of germplasm resources, show-windows for popularization of science, and parks for relaxation and enjoyment.

Wu Chengyih
24 November 1995

Editorial Committee

Honorary Editor-in-Chief: Wu Chengyih

Editor-in-Chief: Tong Fengqin

Deputy Editors-in-Chief: Xu Zaifu   He Shan'an

Editorial Board:

Niu Deshui	Wang Yan	Xu Tianquan
Xu Zaifu	Li Bosheng	Liu Hongmao
Tong Fengqin	He Xingyuan	Du Qingquan
Shao Yingshao	Chen Minghong	Zhang Yijun
Zhang Zhiming	He Shan'an	Huang Zhongliang
Guan Kaiyun	Pan Borong	

Editors:

Wang Yan	Jin Xiaobai	Niu Deshui
Yao Qingxiao	Qian Xiaoyan	Hu Wenkang
Lou Zhiping	Lu Shanfa	Ding Ying

Designer: Li Xinfen

Foreword

Nature provides mankind with precious plant resources, which form the most important material basis for human existence and development. However, the unrestrained exploitation of plant resources by human beings has resulted in serious deterioration of ecological environments and acceleration of plant species extinction on earth. In view of this, botanical gardens are important research bases aiming at plant species collection, conservation, evaluation and utilization.

Since the foundation of the People's Republic of China in 1949, the Chinese Academy of Sciences (CAS) has given emphasis to the development of botanical gardens. Some botanical gardens and arboreta were enlarged or newly established. It was decided that they should orientate to investigation and protection of plant resources, plant introduction and acclimatization, cultivation and utilization of economic plants and public education of plant sciences. In the past over 40 years, with the care and support from the leaders of CAS and research institutes concerned, through the diligence, sweat and toil of the scientists, technicians and other staff members, the 12 botanical gardens and arboreta affiliated with CAS, namely, the Beijing Botanical Garden, the Nanjing Botanical Garden Mem. Sun Yat-Sen, the South China Botanical Garden, the Xishuangbanna Tropical Botanical Garden, the Kunming Botanical Garden, the Wuhan Botanical Garden, the Lushan Botanical Garden the Guilin Botanical Garden, the Dinghushan Arboretum, the Turpan Eremophytes Botanical Garden, the Shenyang Arboretum and the West China Subalpine Botanical Garden have developed into important centres that combine scientific research, plant germplasm conservation and popularization of science. In recent years, according to the trend of development of the relevant branches of science at home and abroad, and to the requirements for economic and social development, the botanical gardens (including the arboreta) of CAS have made new progresses in strengthening the studies on biodiversity conservation and sustainable utilization. They have established good co-operative relationships with other botanical gardens in China and throughout the world, and with international botanical garden organizations. They have become ideal places for academic exchange and international co-operation in researches of plant sciences.

The botanical gardens of CAS are distributed in China from the southeast coast to the northwest gobi desert, from the temperate forest in the northeast to the rain forest in the southwest, covering all of the major biogeographical types of the country. They hold prominent positions among the botanical gardens in

China, in regard to their scale of construction, achievements, research facilities, and their roles in public education.

This picture album illustrates the development of the 12 botanical gardens of CAS, their scientific research programs, garden landscapes, their efforts in public education of plant sciences, international co-operation and academic exchange activities, through concise text and plenty of selected photographs, with their contributions to human existence and development highlighted.

Through the past decades, several generations of botanists have worked hard to establish and develop the botanical gardens of CAS and laid solid foundations for the rapid growth of young botanists today. We particularly cherish the memories of the deceased founders and pioneers of the botanical gardens, whose names are Hu Hsenhsu, Chien Sungshu, Chun Woonyoung, Ching Renchang, Pei Chien, Chen Fenghwai, Yu Tetsun and Tsai Hsetao. We wish to thank the leaders of governments and departments at all levels, who have actively supported the botanical gardens of CAS. We also wish to pay tribute to the scientists and all the staff members who have made achievements in and contributed to scientific research and construction of the botanical gardens of CAS.

The photographs and the text of *The Blossoming Botanical Gardens of the Chinese Academy of Sciences* have been selected from and finalized on the basis of those provided by staff of the 12 botanical gardens affiliated to the Chinese Academy of Sciences, with the joint organization of the Bureau of Science and Technology of Resources and the Environment of CAS and the Working Committee of Botanical Gardens of CAS. The energetic support of the leaders at all levels and of the specialists is gratefully acknowledged here.

Looking to the future, we are confident that the botanical gardens of CAS will show themselves as having the first-class research level and the most attractive garden landscape and scenery.

March 1996

Xu Zhihong

Contents

2   The Blossoming Botanical Gardens of
the Chinese Academy of Sciences

7   Beijing Botanical Garden

23   Nanjing Botanical Garden Mem. Sun Yat-Sen

39   South China Botanical Garden

55   Xishuangbanna Tropical Botanical Garden

71   Kunming Botanical Garden

87   Wuhan Botanical Garden

103   Lushan Botanical Garden

111   Guilin Botanical Garden

119   Dinghushan Arboretum

127   Turpan Eremophytes Botanical Garden

135   Shenyang Arboretum

143   West China Subalpine Botanical Garden

Distribution Scheme Map of the Botanical Gardens of the Chinese Academy of Sciences

❶ Beijing Botanical Garden
❷ Nanjing Botanical Garden Mem. Sun Yat-Sen
❸ South China Botanical Garden
❹ Xishuangbanna Tropical Botanical Garden
❺ Kunming Botanical Garden
❻ Wuhan Botanical Garden
❼ Lushan Botanical Garden
❽ Guilin Botanical Garden
❾ Dinghushan Arboretum
❿ Turpan Eremophytes Botanical Garden
⓫ Shenyang Arboretum
⓬ West China Subalpine Botanical Garden

The Blossoming Botanical Gardens of the Chinese Academy of Sciences

The development of botanical gardens is one of the indications of the development of human civilization. Botanical gardens are closely associated with the development, utilization and protection of plant resources. They are important centres for conservation of plant diversity and for plant introduction and acclimatization. They are the best places for popularization and public education of plant sciences, and for tourism and amenity. They are also the ideal places for internal and international academic exchanges. The Royal Botanic Gardens, Kew of the UK played a significant role in the introduction and research of the Para rubber tree and the development of the rubber industry. This and many other cases have proven that the development of botanical gardens can contribute a great deal to economic and social developments.

China is a large country with rich plant resources. Because of its unique geographical position,on its expansive land of 9 600 000 km^2 are found about 30 000 species of higher plants, which account for 10% of the world flora and rank China the 3rd among all the countries in abundance of plant species. China is also a country with a long history of civilization, and the Shennong Garden of Medicinal Plants of about 2800 years ago is regarded as an embryonic botanical garden in the world.

In China, modern botanical gardens began to appear at the beginning of the 20th century, and have reached 120 in number today, most of which were founded after the 1950s. Of these botanical gardens (including arboreta), 12 are affiliated to the Chinese Academy of Sciences (CAS). They are the Beijing Botanical Garden, the Nanjing Botanical Garden Mem. Sun Yat-Sen*, the South China Botanical Garden, the Xishuangbanna Tropical Botanical Garden, the Kunming Botanical Garden, the Wuhan Botanical Garden, the Lushan Botanical Garden*, the Guilin Botanical Garden*, the Dinghushan Arboretum, the Turpan Eremophytes Botanical Garden, the Shenyang Arboretum, and the West China Subalpine Botanical Garden. Although not great in number, they mostly have a relatively long history, a large size, a strong ability in research and economic development. They hold leading positions in plant diversity conservation, resource development and utilization, basic research and public education.

I. History of Development

Since the foundation in 1949 of the People's Republic of China, the Chinese Academy of Sciences, which is the highest national academic organization for natural sciences, has paid great attention to the construction and development of botanical gardens. By the end of the 1960s, CAS had established 10 botanical gardens, accounting

*Under dual leadership of the Chinese Academy of Sciences and local authority.

for 1/3 of the total number of Chinese botanical gardens at the time. In the 1970s, some of the CAS botanical gardens came under the administration of local authorities, while the Turpan Eremophytes Botanical Garden and the West China Subalpine Botanical Garden were established by CAS in 1976 and 1986 respectively. Today, there are 12 botanical gardens belonging to CAS or under dual leadership of CAS and local authority, which have in total nearly 1600 staff, more than 3000 ha of land, holding over 15 000 taxa in their living plant collections and containing 95 specialized gardens and areas.

In 1963 CAS convened the 1st Meeting on Work of Botanical Gardens, at which *The Working Regulations for Botanical Gardens of CAS (Draft)* was formulated, and the Working Committee of Botanical Gardens of CAS was formed. At the 2nd Meeting on Work of Botanical Gardens of CAS held in 1978, *The* 1978−1985 *Plan for the Development of Botanical Gardens of CAS* was formulated, and the establishment of 4 centres of plant introduction and acclimatization (in Beijing, Nanjing, Guangzhou and Xishuangbanna) was proposed. While working out the Development Programme for the 8th Five-Year Plan Period, the 3rd Meeting on Work of Botanical Gardens called by CAS in 1989 designated researches on plant diversity conservation and sustainable development as part of the major tasks of botanical gardens of CAS.

II . Achievements and Contributions

Through more than 40 years' study, investigation and development, the botanical gardens of CAS have established or are developing their respective features, have formed a network that has made great contributions to the research, conservation, development and utilization of plant resources and public education in China.

1. Centres for plant introduction and research in China

By 1994, over 50% of the elements of the Chinese flora had been introduced into cultivation in botanical gardens of CAS. Among these plants are wild types and close relatives of cultivated crops, various flowers and woody ornamentals, and numerous endemics that could only be found in China. The botanical gardens are living museums and research centres of Chinese plants. They have built in them many specialized gardens holding characteristic collections of plants, such as the Magnoliaceae, cycads and palms in the South China Botanical Garden, conifers in the Lushan Botanical Garden and the Nanjing Botanical Garden Mem. Sun Yat-Sen, bamboos and orchids in the Xishuangbanna Tropical Botanical Garden, camellias in the Kunming Botanical Garden, rhododendrons in the West China Subalpine Botanical Garden, the kunming Botanical Garden and Lushan Botanical Garden wild fruit germplasm and peonies in the Beijing Botanical Garden, aquatic plants and *Actinidi* in the Wuhan Botanical Garden, and the Tamaricaceae in the Turpan Eremophytes Botanical Garden. These have become the important bases for basic researches in botany, for the development, utilization and conservation of plant resources and for public education.

2. Bases for conservation of rare and endangered plants

Since the 1980s, aiming at the frontier of the international development of plant sciences, the CAS botanical gardens have carried out studies on ex situ conservation of rare and endangered plants. The gardens took part in the compilation of the *Chinese Plants Red Data Book* and have conserved ex situ 300 rare and endangered plant species. The South China Botanical Garden, the Guilin Botanical Garden, the Kunming Botanical Garden, the Xishuangbanna Tropical Botanical Garden, the Wuhan Botanical Garden, the Nanjing Botanical Garden Mem. Sun Yat-Sen and the Beijing Botanical Garden each currently hold over 100 species of the protected plants. Scientific record system and microcomputer management system of ex situ conserved plants have been or are being developed in these gardens. Studies and experiments have been conducted on endangerment mechanism, biology and ecology, propagation techniques, artificial imitated communities, and key techniques for effective protection of rare and endangered plants. Comprehensive and in-depth work, such as the investigation on conservation of the Magnoliaceae in the South China Botanical Garden, on genetic diversity of rare and endangered plants in the Beijing Botanical Garden, the Nanjing Botanical Garden Mem. Sun Yat-Sen, the Kunming Botanical Garden and the Xishuangbanna Tropical Botanical Garden, on conservation of threatened plants in limestone mountains carried out in the Guilin Botanical Garden, the formula for comprehensive quantitative assessment of priority of plant conservation and the formula of minimum population for ex situ conservation proposed by the Xishuangbanna Tropical Botanical Garden, the "tripod model" of plant ex situ conservation and the establishment of the provincial key laboratory of plant ex situ conservation in the Nanjing Botanical Garden Mem. Sun Yat-Sen, have been highly commended by colleagues in China and abroad.

3. Sites for public education

With the plant diversity, the rich scientific contents of botany and ecology, and the colourful natural scenes and garden landscapes, the botanical gardens of CAS function as main sites for disseminating scientific knowledge, methodology and ideas, concepts of environment protection and patriotism to students, schoolchildren and the general public. Some of the gardens possess a unique ethnic cultural atmosphere and have become attractive sites for young people to organize activities of winter and summer camps and for the masses to see the sights, have leisure and enjoy themselves. The South China Botanical Garden has been designated as 1 of the 8 new scenes of Guangzhou City, and the Nanjing Botanical Garden Mem. Sun Yat-Sen as 1 of the 40 famous scenes of Nanjing City, while the Xishuangbanna Tropical Botanical Garden and the Lushan Botanical Garden are now known as 1 of the national-level tourist scenic spots. Each year, around 3 million tourists from home and abroad come and visit these botanical gardens, which produces beneficial social effects.

4. Fruitful results of scientific research

By 1994, the botanical gardens of CAS had won nearly 400 prizes at national, ministry and commission (including CAS), provincial and municipal levels for scientific and technological achievements, published more than 200 books and over 3000 papers. They have made great contributions to the development of plant sciences through basic researches and accumulation of information, and to the coordinated development of China's economy and sustainable use of plant resources through studies on plant utilization and conservation. Good examples include the introduction of a tobacco cultivar for tobacco industry (Kunming Botanical Garden) and buffalo grass for lawn-making (Beijing Botanical Garden), the breeding of high-quality grape cultivars (Beijing Botanical Garden), the development of artificial rubber-tea community as a way of planting the 2 crops together in plantations (Xishuangbanna Tropical Botanical Garden), the breeding of new cultivars of kiwifruit and sacred lotus (Wuhan Botanical Garden), the introduction and acclimatization of fine sand-fixing plants (Turpan Eremophytes Botanical Garden), the investigation and utilization of yam resources in China (Nanjing Botanical Garden Mem. Sun Yat-Sen), the introduction and cultivation studies on sandal wood (South China Botanical Garden), the researches on symbiotic nitrogen-fixation of non-leguminous trees (Shenyang Arboretum) and the selection, cultivation and processing techniques of good cultivars of *Ginkgo biloba* (Guilin Botanical Garden). These results have created marked economic and social benefits through wide cultivation of the new plants or extension of the new techniques, or have shown great potentials of application.

5. Frequent international exchanges

Long-term seed and plant exchange programmes are undertaken between the CAS botanical gardens and hundreds of botanical gardens, arboreta, universities and research institutes in more than 70 countries and regions, with thousands of seeds and plants being sent and received each year. Since the 1980s, the botanical gardens have become more and more frequently envolved in international academic exchanges and co-operative researches. Each year the botanical gardens send scores of people to attend international academic conferences, receive thousands of foreign professional visitors and investigators, and are engaged in dozens of co-operative research programmes.

More and more international conferences and symposia are held in or organized by CAS botanical gardens. Chinese botanists in CAS botanical gardens are actively participating in the work of international organizations. These facts can be illustrated by the International Symposium on *Camellia* and the construction of the International Friendship Camellia Garden in Kunming (Kunming Botanical Garden, 1984); the International Symposium on Botanical Gardens — the first symposium of this kind ever held in Asia (Nanjing Botanical Garden Mem. Sun Yat-Sen, 1988); the International Safflower Conference held in Xiangshan, Beijing (Beijing Botanical Garden, 1993); the election of Director Prof. He Shan'an of the Nanjing Botanical Garden Mem. Sun Yat-Sen as President of the Asian Division of the International Association of Botanical Gardens (IABG), and Director Prof. Xu Zaifu of the Xishuangbanna Tropical Botanical Garden as a member of the Council of the Aisan Division of IABG, at the Inaugural Conference of the Division held in Tokyo, Japan in 1991; the election of Prof. He Shan'an as Vice-President of IABG at the 11th International Association of Botanical Gardens Conference held in Wuxi, China in 1993; and the 2nd International Symposium on the Zingiberaceae of Botany 2000 — the Asian Network held in Guangzhou (South China Botanical Garden, 1995).

Close friendship or sister relations are formed between CAS botanical gardens and more than 30 leading botanical gardens of the world, including the Royal Botanic Gardens, Kew and the Royal Botanic Garden Edinburgh of the UK, the Missouri Botanical Garden and the Arnold Arboretum of the USA, the Botanical Gardens of University of Tokyo, Japan, the Royal Botanical Gardens Sydney and the National Botanic Gardens, Canberra, Australia. Large amount of work has been done in co-operation of training, researches on Chinese medicinal herbs, flowers, kiwifruit, exploration and utilization of plant resources, with abundant achievements. The following should particularly be mentioned: the development of the Lotus Garden in California, USA, with the help of the Wuhan Botanical Garden; the export of ornamental aquatic plants to over 10 countries in Asia, Europe and America by the same Garden; the building up of Chinese plant collections in the Toyama Central Botanical Garden of Japan and the Royal Botanic Garden Edinburgh of the UK with the help of the Kunming Botanical Garden; and the presentation of a marble statue of Chinese herbalist Li Shizhen by Gifu Pharmaceutical University, Japan to the Wuhan Botanical Garden in 1993 in commemoration of the 450th anniversary of his birth.

Comprehensive exchange and co-operation with colleagues in foreign countries on modernization in management of botanical gardens, popularization of science and public education, publication of books and periodicals are also going on.

BEIJING
BOTANICAL GARDEN

Introduction

The Beijing Botanical Garden, affiliated with the Institute of Botany, Chinese Academy of Sciences, is situated southwest of Xiangshan, 18 km from the city centre of Beijing, at lat. 39° 48′ N, long. 116° 28′ E, and 76 m above sea level. The climate is temperate continental, the annual mean temperature being 11.6℃, the mean temperature for January −3.7℃, the extreme minimum temperature −17.5℃, the mean temperature for July 26.7℃, the extreme maximum temperature 41.3℃, the annual precipitation 634.2 mm, and the relative humidity 43%−79%.

The Garden originated from a small botanical garden which was built inside the Beijing Zoo in 1925 and which came under the Chinese Academy of Sciences in 1949. The present site was chosen in 1955 to establish what was then decided to bear the name of Beijing Botanical Garden, Institute of Botany, Chinese Academy of Sciences. Prof. Yu Tetsun, who became the 1st Director of the Garden, and other prominent botanists, including Prof. Chien Sungshu, Prof. Hu Hsenhsu, Prof. Ching Renchang, Prof. Chen Fenghwai, gave their guidance and contributed their efforts to ensure the rapid development of the Garden.

Researches are conducted on exsitu conservation of rare and endangered plants, utilization of wild plant resources, introduction and acclimatization of economically important plants, especially those from northern China. The plants are arranged and displayed according to the principles of plant ecology and landscape aesthetics. It has become a centre for studies on ex situ conservation and sustainable use of northern China plant diversity and for public education on these themes.

The Garden will eventually cover an area of 119 ha; but currently it occupies 56.4 ha of the land, with 20.7 ha of display areas, 17.2 ha of experimental field, 1820 m^2 of display greenhouses, and 3000 m^2 of experiment greenhouses. Among the display areas are the Arboretum, the Perennial Garden, the Rose Garden, the Peony Garden, the Chinese Medicinal Herb Garden, the Wild Fruit Tree Resources Section, the Environment-Protection Plants Garden, the Aquatic and Climbing Plants Garden, the Rare and Endangered Plants Section, the Tropical and Subtropical Plant Houses. The living collection contains 6000 taxa. The Garden is equipped with tissue culture facilities, an underground seed storage room and an experimental winery. The Library holds 25 000 books and 13 000 periodicals. The Seed Herbarium has 75 000 accessions of 22 500 taxa, ranking 1st in Asia and 3rd in the world.

There are 110 staff members, of whom 31 are senior researchers and technicians, 45 are intermediate and junior ones. Since its foundation, 70 books and 563 papers have been published. More than 70 research projects have achieved results; 41 of them, such as the breeding of new grape cultivars, the collection, preservation and evaluation of safflower germplasm, the introduction and utilization of buffalo grass, the breeding of sweet sorghum, and the research of natural antioxidant, have won significant awards. With the reform and opening-up of the country, the Garden is actively engaged in international exchanges and academic activities. Seed exchange programmes are established with over 300 botanical gardens and other institutions in 46 countries. Each year the Garden receives 250 000−300 000 visitors from home and abroad.

Making the most of the preponderance of scientific knowledge and technical know-how, the Garden has been extending its research results into the market. Good social and economic benefits have been achieved through contracted work of landscape design and construction, production, sale and export of flowers, nursery stock, seeds and handicrafts of dried flowers. These activities have contributed to beautification of the capital and enrichment of people's life, and strengthened the position of the Garden for further development.

Add: Beijing Botanical Garden, Institute of Botany, Chinese Academy of Sciences,
　　　20 Nanxincun,Xiangshan, Beijing 100093, China
Tel : (86-10) 62591431
Fax: (86-10) 62590348

Beijing Botanical Garden

Paeonia.

The Peony Garden

The Peony Garden covers an area of 0.1 ha. More than 100 cultivars of tree peony and over 20 cultivars of herbaceous peony are cultivated here. They are well-known traditional flowers in China. Their roots are used medicinally .

A view of the Peony Garden.

Paeonia suffruticosa 'Xi Xia Ying Ri'.

Paeonia lactiflora 'Fen Yin Zhen'.

Beijing Botanical Garden

Rose.

The Rose Garden

The Rose Garden covers an area of 0.6 ha. More than 400 rose cultivars are grown here. Roses are regarded as the queen of flowers for their ornamental value. They are also used medicinally.

Rose 'Fang Chun'.

Rose 'Peace'.

Rose 'Jia Chun'.

The Arboretum

The Arboretum covers an area of 12.6 ha, with a collection of more than 1000 species of trees and shrubs belonging to 196 genera and 66 families, including some well-known plants such as *Pinus griffithii*, *Eucommia ulmoides, Metasequoia glyptostroboides, Rhus typhina, Abelia chinensis*, double-flowered lilac (*Syringa oblata* cv.) and *Kolkwitzia amabilis.*

Magnolia liliflora.

Rhododendron mucronulatum.

Staghorn sumac (*Rhus typhina*).

White flowering peach (*Prunus persica* 'Albo-plena').

Staghorn sumac (*Rhus typhina*).

The Pavilion in the Pinetum.

Late lilac (*Syringa villosa*).

Magnolia denudata.

Weigela floribunda.

The Perennial Garden

The Perennial Garden covers an area of 1 ha, with a collection of more than 600 species and cultivars of perennial flowers. It ranks the first in China in respect of the number of taxa. Well- known plants growing here include hybrid daylilies (*Hemerocallis*), lilies (*Lilium*), tulips (*Tulipa*), oriental poppy (*Papaver orientalis*), *Clematis* and *Phlox*.

Daylily (*Hemerocallis*) hybrid.

A view of the Perennial Garden.

Summer perennial phlox (*Phlox paniculata*).

Tulips (*Tulipa gesnerian*).

Clematis hybrid.

Lilium davidii.

Pink-flowered hyacinth (*Hyacinthus orientalis*).

White-flowered hyacinth (*Hyacinthus orientalis*).

Lilium regale.

Autumn crocus (*Colchicum autumnale*).

Ginseng (*Panax ginseng*), a medicinal plant.

The Chinese Medicinal Herb Garden

It covers an area of 1 ha, with more than 450 species of medicinal plants cultivated here, including the well-known ginseng (*Panax ginseng*), *Acanthopanax senticosus, Schisandra chinensis, Astragalus chinensis, Pinellia ternata, Gynostemma pentaphyllum, Apocynum venitum, Polygonum multiflorum* and Ural licorice (*Glycyrrhiza uralensis*).

Tussilago farfara, a medicinal plant.

A view of the Chinese Medicinal Herb Garden.

Amorphophallus virosus, a medicinal plant.

Pulsatilla chinensis, a medicinal plant.

The Environment-Protection Plants Garden

It covers an area of 2 ha, with more than 100 species of plants resistant or sensitive to air-pollution. The Garden is composed of 6 plots, featuring plants resistant to sulphur dioxide, such as *Koelreuteria paniculata, Toona sinensis, Paulownia tomentosa* and *Lagerstroemia indica*; plants resistant to chlorine and gaseous hydrochloric acid, such as *Clerodendrum trichotomum, Forsythia suspensa* and London plane (*Platanus × hybrida*); plants resistant to fluoride; plants resistant to ozone; plants resistant to dusts, such as *Pinus armandii* and *Sabina chinensis* 'Pyramidalis'; and plants sensitive to air-pollution.

An environment-protection plant.

Lagerstroemia indica 'Rosey'.

Pygmy waterlily (*Nymphaea capensis*)
from the tropics.

The Aquatic Garden

The Aquatic Garden occupies an area of 0.3 ha, with over 160 taxa of aquatic flowers and climbing plants. There are more than 40 cultivars of sacred lotus (*Nelumbo*), 20 cultivars of waterlilies (*Nymphaea*), as well as giant waterlily (*Victoria amazonica*), Chinese ancient lotus and *Euryale ferox*.

A view of the Aquatic Garden.

Sacred lotus (*Nelumbo nucifera*)'Xiao Bi Lian'. →

← Giant waterlily (*Victoria amazonica*), a world-famous ornamental plant, with leaves to 2 m in diameter and capable of supporting a load of 40 kg (the girl in the photo is aged 6). It was introduced to the Beijing Botanical Garden for the first time in 1959.

The Display Greenhouses

The complex of the Display Greenhouses covers a total area of 2600 m², with a collection of over 1000 taxa of plants from the world that have ornamental, economic and scientific values. It is an important part of the Beijing Botanical Garden, providing sites for biodiversity conservation, enjoyment, public education, international academic exchanges and friendly contacts between peoples of the world. The 14 display houses include those for palms, cacti and succulents, foliage plants, ferns and orchids.

Primula × polyantha.

The Foliage Plant House.

The Cactus and Succulent House.

Caladium hortulanum.

The Palm House.

Cymbidium tracyanum.

Phalaenopsis sp.

A cultivar of *Calceolaria* × *herbeohybrida.*

Another cultivar of *Calceolaria* × *herbeohybrida.*

The male plant of *Cycas panzhihuaensis*, a nationally protected species.

The female plant of *Cycas panzhihuaensis*, a nationally protected species.

'Jingyu', a new grape cultivar.

'Jingxiu', a new grape cultivar.

'Kezhi No.1', an interspecific hybrid cultivar of kiwifruit (*Actinidia*).

Achievements in Scientific Research

Carthamus tinctorius 'FO-2', a new safflower cultivar.

NANJING
BOTANICAL GARDEN
MEM.SUN YAT-SEN

Introduction

The Nanjing Botanical Garden Mem. Sun Yat-Sen of Jiangsu Province and the Chinese Academy of Sciences was named after Dr Sun Yat-Sen, the great forerunner of the Chinese democratic revolution. It was rebuilt in 1954, with the Sun Yat-Sen Memorial Botanical Garden, originally founded in 1929, as its predecessor. It is now under the dual leadership of Jiangsu Province and the Chinese Academy of Sciences.

The Botanical Garden is located at lat. 32° 07′ N, long. 118° 48′ E, and 30 − 40 m altitude, with annual mean temperature of 15.4℃ and annual precipitation of 1000 mm. The site is in the scenic area of the eastern suburb of Nanjing, facing the peaceful Qianhu Lake and the old city wall, with the solemn Sun Yat-sen Mausoleum in the distance, and lying at the foot of the towering Mount Zhongshan.

As one of the leading botanical gardens in China, it has developed into a research centre of northern and middle subtropical plants, which combines features of a modern botanical garden and an institute of botany, and focuses on studies of plant resources and the environment. The Garden has an area of 186 ha, with 2000 m^2 of greenhouses of which 1397 m^2 are for display, and 2 ha of experimental nursery. About 100 000 plants of 3000 taxa, belonging to 913 genera and 188 families, are in cultivation. Accomplished are 7 specialized gardens and sections: the Ornamental Plants Section, the Plant Systematic Garden, the Arboretum, the Pinetum, the Medicinal Plants Garden, the Rare and Endangered Plants Section, and the Display Greenhouses. These will be joined by the Garden for the Visually Handicapped and the Penjing Garden, which are under construction. Researches are conducted in departments and laboratories on plant taxonomy, plant acclimatization and breeding, medicinal plants, phytoecology, phytochemistry and ex situ conservation of plants. The Herbarium houses over 600 000 sheets of plant specimens, and the Library contains 45 000 volumes of books and periodicals. The Nanjing Zhongshan International Botanical Gardens Club and the Jiangsu Zhongshan International Holiday Club also have been set up here.

The Garden staff has 317 members, among whom 207 are researchers and technicians. Dozens of postgraduate students have been enrolled and pursued researches for doctor or master degrees since 1980.

In the past more than 40 years, over 280 research results were achieved, of which 71 won national, provincial or ministerial awards. The major ones include the utilization researches on resources of *Dioscorea* and on *Ginkgo biloba* leaves. Specialists of the Garden have been involved in writing on 7 families of the *Flora of China* and volumes 1− 9 of the *Medicinal Flora of China*, and have published 100 books and 1330 papers. The Garden is responsible for the *Journal of Plant Resources and Environment*. Computer management systems for botanical garden living plant records and planting maps have been developed and established here.

Programmes for exchange of living plants, plant specimens and publications with 600 institutions in over 60 countries are established. The Nanjing Botanical Garden Mem. Sun Yat-sen has formed sister relationship with the Missouri Botanical Garden, USA, invited Dr. P. H. Raven, Director of the latter, as its Honorary Director, and developed friendly relationship with the Botanical Garden of University of British Columbia, Canada, and the Botanical Gardens of University of Tokyo, Japan. Jiangsu Pipa Horticultural Company Ltd. is a joint venture formed with a Canadian enterprise to explore and utilize plant resources. Academic exchanges and collaborations have been established with over 30 countries. The Garden is also 1 of the 4 centres of the Sino-American joint project of the English edition of *Flora of China.*

Each year the Garden receives 250 000 visitors from home and abroad. It has been designated as a base for science education, which attracts youngsters and schoolchildren to participate in activities for gaining scientific knowledge.

Add: Nanjing Botanical Garden Mem. Sun Yat-Sen, Jiangsu Province and Chinese Academy of Sciences,

1 QianhuHoucun, Zhongshan Men Wai, Nanjing, Jiangsu 210014, China

Tel : (86-25) 4432128

Fax: (86-25) 4432074

Deng Xiaoping visiting the Nanjing Botanical Garden Mem. Sun Yat-Sen (1985).

The Garden for the Visually Handicapped.

The hall for public education activities.

Shizhen Guan, an exhibition hall commemorating Li Shizhen, the great herbalist of Ming Dynasty.

The Garden for the Visually Handicapped.

Unveiling of the Memorial of the International Symposium on Botanical Gardens, in front of the Main Building of the Garden (September 1988).

Prof. Peter H. Raven of the Missouri Botanical Garden, USA, was invited to be Honorary Director of the Nanjing Botanical Garden Mem. Sun Yat-Sen (July 1992).

Nanjing Botanical Garden Mem. Sun Yat-Sen

The Rose Garden and aquatic plants.

The Ornamental Plants Section

The Ornamental Plants Section is the main scenic area for visitors in the Botanical Garden. The Main Building and the Herbarium stand in the centre of this Section. More than 600 plant species and cultivars are displayed in an area of 13 ha. The most prominent include roses (*Rosa*), Prunus, Santa Cruz giant waterlily (*Victoria cruziana*), Japanese maple (*Acer palmatum*), Chinese viburnum (*Viburnum macrocephalum*) and Fortune firethorn (*Pyracantha fortuneana*).

Hypericum chinense in bloom.

The avenue lined with trees of *Ginkgo biloba*.

One of the main display areas in the Section.

The Plant Systematic Garden

The Plant Systematic Garden has an area of 6 ha. More than 300 species of seed plants belonging to 204 genera and 85 families are grown here. Among them are *Torreya grandis,* golden larch (*Pseudolarix amabilis*), Chinese tuliptree (*Liriodendron chinense*), Chinese yew (*Taxus chinensis*) and star magnolia (*Magnolia stellata*).

Hydrangea macrophylla var. *hortensia.*

The Plant Systematic Garden.

Hydrangea macrophylla var. *hortensia.*

Langya elm (*Ulmus chenmoui*), endemic to Anhui and Jiangsu, is a fine timber tree.

Idesia polycarpa, distributed in Henan, Shaanxi, Gansu, the Changjiang River valley and further south in China, is used for ornament.

The Arboretum

In the area of more than 10 ha, over 340 taxa of woody plants native to eastern China are cultivated. It is dominated by broad-leaved evergreen and deciduous trees and shrubs of the Fagaceae, Lauraceae, Magnoliaceae and Aceraceae, serving as a base for scientific studies on introduction and acclimatization of woody plants of the middle and northern subtropical regions.

A part of the Arboretum.

Magnolia cylindrica, distributed in Henan, Zhejiang, Anhui, Jiangxi and Fujian, is a handsome ornamental tree with flower buds and flowers used for medicine and perfume.

Malus halliana, distributed in Jiangsu, Zhejiang, Anhui, Hubei, Sichuan, Yunnan and Shaanxi, is a fine ornamental shrub.

The Pinetum

In the 7 ha land of the Pinetum have been conserved 100 coniferous taxa, including *Cupressus lusitanica* 'Zhongshan', dawn redwood (*Metasequoia glyptostroboides*), pond cypress (*Taxodium ascendens*) and deciduous cypress (*T. distichum*).

Keteleeria davidiana, occurring in Shaanxi, Gansu, Sichuan, Guizhou and Hunan, is an ornamental and timber tree.

The Pinetum.

Metasequoia glyptostroboides is a relict plant found in Sichuan and Hubei. It is a fast-growing tree for timber and ornament.

Cupressus lusitanica 'Zhongshan', a fast-growing timber tree bred by the Botanical Garden, is also used for ornament.

The Medicinal Plants Garden.

Medicinal Plants Garden

The Medicinal Plants Garden, with an area of 2 ha, has more than 600 species of Chinese medicinal herbs belonging to 429 genera of 131 families in the collection. Some of the important medicinal herbs growing here are Anhui barberry (*Berberis chingii*), *Camptotheca accuminata*, Chinese horse chestnut (*Aesculus chinensis*), peltate yam (*Dioscorea zingiberensis*), *Paris polyphylla* and Chinese goldthread (*Coptis chinensis*).

Evodia rutaecarpa occurs in the Changjiang River valley and further south in China.

Adenophora polyantha occurs in Liaoning, Hebei, Shaanxi, Shandong, Anhui and Jiangsu.

Magnolia officinalis occurs in Shaanxi, Gansu, Hubei, Hunan and Sichuan.

The Display Greenhouses

Within the 1500 m² of the greenhouses are 845 tropical and subtropical species belonging to 347 genera of 105 families. The display combines scientific contents with horticultural arts, showing fantastic flowers and rare trees such as begonias (*Begonia*), bird-of-paradise flower (*Strelitzia reginae*), golden candle (*Pachystachys lutea*), yellow-flowered camellia(*Camellia nitidissima*) and coffee tree (*Coffea arabica*).

× *Heliochia* 'Ackermannii'.

Inside display greenhouse.

Red orchid cactus (× *Heliochia* 'Ackermannii').

Bird-of-paradise flower (*Strelitzia reginae*) from South Africa.

Yellow-flowered camellia (*Camellia nitidissima*).

Cacti.

Blackberries (*Rubus* spp.), introduced from North America in 1986, produce edible fruits that can also be processed into juice, jam, jelly and wine.

The Section for Breeding of Economic Plants

This Section has an area of 10 ha, with the function of collecting and conserving germplasm of subtropical economic plants. Collections of Chinese chestnut (*Castanea mollissima*), pecan (*Carya illinoensis*) and blackberry (*Rubus*) have been established to provide material for studies on acclimatization, breeding and genetic variation.

Chinese chestnut (*Castanea mollissima*) 'Jiu Jia Zhong', a superior cultivar selected from materials from Jiangsu.

Pecan tree (*Carya illinoensis*), introduced from North America in 1983, produces edible nuts.

Bermuda grass (*Cynodon dactylon*) 'Pa Di Qing', a new cultivar for lawn, was bred by the Garden.

The Rare and Endangered Plants Section

The Section has an area of about 7 ha. Over 80 nationally protected species have been conserved here. Among them are well-known species such as dove tree (*Davidia involucrata*), *Magnolia zenii*, *Tapiscia sinensis*, *Sinojackia xylocarpa* and *Emmenopterys henryi*.

Sinocalycanthus chinensis, occurring only in eastern China, is an ornamental plant.

The Rare and Endangered Plants Section.

Shaniodendron subaequale, a rare species, occurs in Jiangsu, Zhejiang and Anhui.

Tapiscia sinensis, occurring in Henan, Shaanxi, Gansu, the Changjiang River valley and further south, is a fine ornamental tree.

Dove tree (*Davidia involucrata*), distributed in Shaanxi, Hubei, Hunan, Sichuan and Guizhou, is a world-famous ornamental plant.

Euptelea pleiospermum occurs in Hebei, Gansu, Shaanxi, Zhejiang, Anhui, Henan, Hunan, Hubei, Guizhou, Sichuan, Yunnan and Tibet.

Torreya jackii, occurring in Zhejiang and Fujian, is a precious garden plant.

Liriodendron chinense, a precious tree for ornament.

Emmenopterys henryi, a nationally protected plant.

Aesculus chinensis, distributed in Hebei and Shaanxi, is an ornamental tree with seeds for medicinal use.

Pyracantha crenulata.

Reevesia pubescens, an ornamental tree.

Corylopsis sinensis, distributed in Anhui, Zhejiang, Jiangxi, Fujian, Hunan, Hubei, Guangdong, Guangxi and Guizhou, is used for ornament.

Rabbit-eye blueberry (*Vaccinium ashei*), a species endemic to China.

SOUTH CHINA
BOTANICAL GARDEN

Introduction

The South China Botanical Garden is affiliated to the South China Institute of Botany, Chinese Academy of Sciences, and is located in Longyandong, 15 km northwest of the city centre of Guangzhou, at lat. 23° 10′ N, long. 113° 21′ E, 20-327 m above sea level, with a southern subtropical monsoon climate of 22℃ annual mean temperature, 38℃ extreme maximum temperature, 0.8℃ extreme minimum temperature, and 1600 - 1800 mm annual precipiation. The complex topography, warm climate and ample rainfall make it an ideal place for plant introduction and acclimatization.

The Garden was founded in 1956 on the initiative of scientists Prof. Chun Woonyoung, Prof. He Chunnian and others. With the emphasis on scientific study and utilization of tropical and subtropical plant resources of South China, it aims at the full development of its functions of research, garden construction and planting, public education and economic development. Botanist Prof. Chen Fenghwai was in charge of the Garden for many years.

On its 300 ha of land have been introduced 5000 taxa of tropical and subtropical plants. Fourteen specialized display gardens and sections have been set up: Palms, Medicinal Plants, Gymnosperms, Bamboos, Economic Plants, Woody Ornamental Plants, Relict Plants, Tropical Plants, the Pugang Nature Reserve, Shade Plants, Polution-tolerant Plants, the Orchid Garden, the Ginger Garden, and the Cycad Garden. The Botanical Garden has 7032 m^2 of office and laboratory buildings, 6387 m^2 of greenhouses and shading shelters, 1775 m^2 of the Scientists' Hotel and 6610 m^2 of living quarters.

Among the 173 staff members are 11 senior researchers and technicians, 28 intermediate and 36 junior ones.

Since 1980, 37 projects have been conducted, with priority given to utilization of tropical and subtropical plants, the theory and practice of acclimatization and conservation, studies on biodiversity, germplasm preservation, and cultivation, propagation and breeding of economic plants. Twenty three results have been achieved, and 15 of them have been awarded national, provincial or ministerial prizes. Published papers amount to 257.

The Garden has developed seed and plant exchange programmes with over 50 countries and regions. It has twined with the Kadoorie Farm and Botanic Garden in Hong Kong, thus enlarging its channel of plant introduction from South Asia.

The rich plant collections with their great scientific significance, displayed through the beautiful landscape, have made the Garden very popular among people of all walks of life. It was designated in 1986 as 1 of the 8 new scenes of Guangzhou City , and receives 400 000-500 000 visitors each year.

It is planned that in a few years the plant collections will expand to include 8000 taxa. A central laboratory of plant introduction and acclimatization, a biodiversity research base, acycad propagation centre, as well as 10 additional specialized floristic gardens of South China plants, will be established. The South China Botanical Garden will become an important research centre of plant sciences in China, and a favourite tourist site attracting 1 million people annually.

Add: South China Botanical Garden, South China Institute of Botany, Chinese Academy of Sciences,

Longyandong,Shahe, Guangzhou, Guangdong 510520, China

Tel : (86-20) 87713790, (86-20) 87705693

Fax : (86-20) 87713797

South China Botanical Garden

A beautiful scene of plants, the pavilion, the bridge and the calm lake.

The Garden Gate.

The South China Botanical Garden–1 of the 8 famous new scenes in Guangzhou.

Ficus drupacea var. *pubescens*, a good tropical ornamental tree.

Alpinia henryi × *A.polyantha.*

Michelia shiluensis, an endemic tree to Hainan, with shapely crown, is used in gardens and planted by streets.

Chuniophoenix hainanensis, a threatened plant endemic to Hainan.

South China Botanical Garden

Flowering banana (*Musa coccinea*), a showy plant with erect flower head.

The Lath Veranda for Shade Plants

It occupies 2000 m², with about 100 taxa of foliage plants.

The Lath Veranda for Ferns occupies more than 1000 m², having various ferns, including some rare and endangered species such as *Alsophila spinulosa*, in display.

Stromanthe sanguinea, a shade plant with leaves olive-green above, blood-red beneath and producing white flowers with salmon-red bracts.

Neoregelia carolinae, one of the most attractive members of the colourful Bromeliaceae.

Bird's nest fern (*Asplenium nidus*), one of the most common ornamental ferns in humid tropical regions.

The Woody Ornamental Plants Section

It occupies 2 ha and is one of the most colourful sections, where there are always some flowers open throughout the year. It holds 150 taxa of ornamental trees and shrubs, such as *Bauhinia blakeana, B. variegata, Bougainvillea spectabilis* and its varieties, *Lagerstroemia speciosa* and *Erythrina indica*.

Yellow oleander (*Thevetia Peruviana*).

Variegated-leaf croton (*Codiaeum variegatum*), a beautiful tropical shrub with highly ornamental leaves in different colours and shapes.

Ardisia densilepidotula, a shrub with flowers clustered like umbrellas.

Woodfordia fruticosa, an ornamental shrub with small red flowers along the stems and branches.

Mussaenda erosa, with white leaf-like sepals and golden-yellow corolla.

The rubber tree *(Ficus elastica),* a large tropical ornamental tree, can be grown as a pot plant when young.

A view of the Woody Ornamental Plants Section.

Yellow oleander (*Thevetia peruviana*), a native of Mexico, is a tropical evergreen shrub with linear, shining green leaves and funnel-shaped orange-yellow flowers all year round.

The Palm Section

This Section occupies 3 ha, holding nearly 100 species of palms, such as *Roystonea regia, Archontophoenix alexandrae, Arenga pinnata* and *Chuniophoenix hainanensis,* which are typical of tropical and subtropical landscapes.

Cuban royal palm (*Roystonea regia*) trees line the road.

A view of the Palm Section.

South China Botanical Garden

The Relict Plants Section

This Section occupies 1.6 ha, with more than 20 species of relict plants, including the living fossil *Metasequoia glyptostroboides*.

The Bamboo Garden

It covers an area of 15 ha, with 220 taxa of *Bambusa* and other bamboos, mainly those growing in clumps and usable for construction and weaving, or producing edible young shoots.

The Bamboo Garden.

A view of the Relict Plants Section.

A view of the Bamboo Garden.

The Xerophytes House

Xerophytes.

Bird-of-paradise tree (*Strelitzia nicolai*), a native of South Africa, is a banana-like perennial with white flowers in a horizontal boat-shaped bract.

Variegated false agave (*Furcraea selloa* 'Marginata'), a pretty succulent with rosetted leaves more than 1 m long and with golden margins.

A view of the Xerophytes House.

Cattleya from South America, with many cultivars, producing large bright-coloured flowers of great ornamental value and suitable for use as cut flowers.

The Orchid Garden

The Orchid Garden has an area of 5600 m², with nearly 300 species of tropical and subtropical terrestrial epiphytic and aerial orchids such as *Cymbidium, Cattleya, Vanda, Dendrobium* and *Epidendrum* in display.

Cymbidium floribundum, one of the best cymbidiums, with many flowers on erect peduncles.

Epidendrum cochleatum, a native of tropical Central America, is a very special epiphytic orchid, producing flowers with a shell-like lip.

Arachnis clarkei, a native of Yunnan, is an epiphytic orchid. The white flowers are spider-shaped, with dense brown-red spots on petals. It blooms in September and October and lasts for one month.

Paphiopedilum villosum, a native of Thailand, is one of the terrestrial orchids, producing large flowers with a pouched lip and lasting more than 2 months. It prefers a moist and shady environment.

A corner of the Orchid Garden.

South China Botanical Garden

The Ginger Garden.

The Ginger Garden

The Ginger Garden has an area of 2.5 ha. There are 120 species in 18 genera of the Zingiberaceae introduced from China and the world, including medicinal, aromatic and ornamental plants such as *Alpinia, Hedychium* and *Zingiber.*

Alpinia katsumadai, a shade ornamental plant, produces seeds of medicinal use.

Globba barthei grows well in moist and semi-shade places. The plant looks like a dancing girl when in bloom, and is a good pot plant.

Curcuma kwangsiensis, distributed in Guangxi, is a sun plant with showy flowers. The rhizome is used medicinally.

The Cycad Garden

The Cycad Garden has an area of 1.5 ha, with nearly 40 cycad species belonging to 7 genera and 3 families introduced from home and abroad. There are over 1000 cycad plants more than 2 m high that bloom and bear seeds every year. It is one of the most attractive specialized gardens.

Cycas revoluta, a native of East Asia, is a very attractive and popular ornamental plant.

Cycas pectinata.

Cycas taiwaniana, a nationlly protected plant.

South China Botanical Garden

Manglietiastrum sinicum, a native of Yunnan and a rare species under national protection, is the only member of the genus, and a good timbe tree.

The Magnolia Garden

The Magnolia Garden has an area of 12 ha and has nearly 130 species of magnoliaceous plants, including 23 rare and endangered species such as *Manglietiastrum sinicum*. It is one of the largest bases in the world for the conservation of magnoliaceous germplasm.

Manglietia grandis, a native of Yunnan , is an endangered species under national protection.

Manglietia megaphylla, a rare species native to Yunnan , is a timber tree and ornamental street tree.

A view of the Magnolia Garden.

A corner of the nursery for introduction and propagation.

The Nursery

It occupies 28 ha and is an important base for producing various plants.

Gymnocalycium mihanovichii.

Massive production of red cap cactus (*Gymnocalycium mihanovichii*) and other succulent plants.

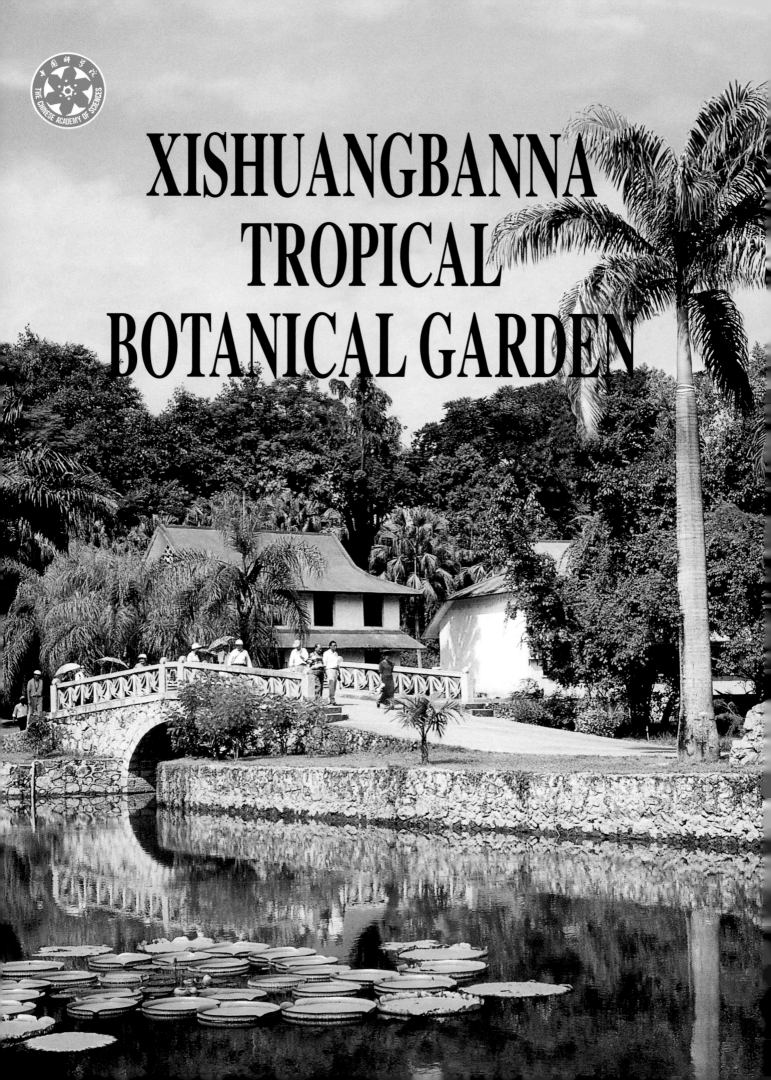

XISHUANGBANNA TROPICAL BOTANICAL GARDEN

Introduction

The Xishuangbanna Tropical Botanical Garden of the Chinese Academy of Sciences is situated in Xishuangbanna Dai Autonomous Prefecture, Yunnan Province, at lat. 21° 41′ N, long. 101° 25′ E, and 570 m altitude, with annual mean temperature of 21.4℃, annual precipitation of 1556.8 mm and mean relative humidity of 83%. The site is a gourd-shaped peninsula almost totally surrounded by the Luosuo River, a branch of the Mekong River. Still having large areas covered with tropical rain forest, it is an ideal place for studying tropical plants. Since its establishment in 1959 under the leadership of the well-known botanist Prof. Tsai Hsetao, the Botanical Garden has been engaged in scientific research, germplasm preservation, public education and scientific exploitation, and has developed its typical tropical landscape and colourful ethnic features.

Among the 424 staff members are 207 researchers and technicians, including 50 of senior rank and 64 of intermediate rank. In total more than 3000 taxa of tropical plants introduced from home and abroad are cultivated in the Garden, with an area of 900 ha. Picturesque scenes are composed of specialized gardens and sections, such as the Tropical Fruit Resources Section, the Orchid Resources Section, the Palm Section, the Oil Plants Section, the Dipterocarpaceae Section, the Spice Section, the Medicinal Plants Section, the Bamboo Section, and the Rare and Endangered Plants Ex Situ Conservation Section. There are also Research Departments of Landscape Gardening, Ex Situ Conservation of Plants, Agroforestry, Forest Ecology, the Ailaoshan Forest Ecosystem Research Station, the Xishuangbanna Minitoring Station of Tropical Rain Forest Biodiversity, and the Southeast Asia Biodiversity Research Centre, jointly built by CAS and Yunnan Province. In addition, the Herbarium of Tropical Botany, the Library, the Plant Ecology and Physiology Laboratory, the Phytochemistry Laboratory, the Seed Bank, plantations of tropical economic plants and the experimental field for agroforestry provide good facilities for research workers of plants.

The Garden aims at tropical plant diversity conservation and sustainable use, combining these with ethnic culture preservation and social and economic development. Since the foundation of the Garden, 585 projects have been undertaken and 283 achievements have been made. The 75 important achievements winning national, provincial or ministerial prizes include researches on model of artificial rubber-tea community, resources of dragon's blood in China and propagation and conservation of *Parashorea chinensis* and *Alsophila spinulosa*. Twenty-nine books and 1300 papers have been published.

Seed and living plant exchanges are carried out with 54 countries. The Garden has become an important centre for academic activities, where were held the 1st and 2nd Meetings on Work of Botanical Gardens, the Symposium on Ethnobotany, the Symposium on Plant Diversity Conservation, and other international symposiums and conferences. Frequent academic exchanges are made with botanical gardens and academic institutions in the USA, Japan, the UK, Thailand and other countries.

With its tropical flowers, beautiful scenes, intense ethnic flavour and rich scientific substance, the Garden has been designated as a national-level tourist scenic spot since 1991, and now receives 250 000–300 000 tourists a year. A tourist souvenir market and the Cultural Museum of Forest Ethnobotany have been built, with the audio-video Biodiversity Exhibition Hall and other scheduled to be constructed, to meet the increasing demand of tourism.

The Xishuangbanna Candle Scientific Development Company Ltd., the Xishuangbanna Gourd Peninsula Tourist Company, the Service Centre and the Pharmaceutical Manufactory have been set up in the Garden and are engaged in the production of tropical fruits, flowers, spices, herbal medicines, and in providing tourist services. They have contributed to the development of the society, the local economy and the Garden itself.

Add: Xishuangbanna Tropical Botanical Garden, Chinese Academy of Sciences,

Menglun Town, Mengla County, Yunnan 666303, China

Tel : (86-691) 8715460

Fax: (86-691) 8715070

President Jiang Zemin plants a tree of *Ormosia hosiei* to show his solicitude for scientists working in the border areas of China (1989).

Premier Li Peng visits the Garden and plants a tree of *Mesua ferrea* for commemoration (1996).

Xishuangbanna Tropical Botanical Garden

A granite sculpture entitled "Surveying in Tropical Rain Forest", depicting Prof. Tsai Hsetao and his colleagues conducting field investigation.

Highlights of the Garden

A man-made tropical rain forest.

The East Gate of the Garden.

A night view of the drawbridge over the Luosuo River that serves as a path through the West Gate to the Garden.

From rubber tree plantation to man-made tropical rain forest. A view illustrating the gradual increase in complexity of artificial plant communities.

Scientific Research

A girl of Hani nationality thanks scientists of the Garden for improving the quality of pomelo (*Citrus grandis*) trees in her courtyard garden.

Scientists are conducting field investigation in the tropical rain forest.

The Garden pioneered in China in researches on agroforestry systems, with the "rubber plus tea" model proved to be the most successful.

The Garden has conducted researches on sustainable development of rural areas, and has helped the local ethnic peoples develop new cash crops.

Xishuangbanna Tropical Botanical Garden

The Palm Garden has an area of 4.6 ha, and holds approximately 150 species of palms, including talipot palm (*Corypha umraculifera*),wine palm (*Borassus flabellifera*) and royal palm(*Roystonea regia*).

The Palm Garden.

The Shade Plants Garden has an area of 0.9 ha. About 400 species of native shade plants from tropical rain forests have been collected and cultivated. About 250 species are epiphytic orchids, and the rest belong to the Araceae, Zingiberaceae and so on.

The Tropical Orchard (about 5 ha) holds more than 100 species of valuable tropical fruit trees, including rambutan (*Nephelium lappaceum*), mango (*Mangifera indica*) and egg-fruit (*Lucuma nervosa*).

The Area for Ex Situ Conservation of Endangered Plants of Southern Yunnan (90 ha), established in a remaining tropical rain forest fragment, contains about 50 species that have been listed under natonal protection, and serves researches on ex situ conservation of rare and endangered plants.

About 100 species of bamboos, including *Chimonobambusa quadrangularis*, *Dendrocalamus hamiltonii* and *Dinochloa bannaensis,* are cultivated in the Garden of Bamboos, which has an area of 6.0 ha.

The Tropical Aquatic Section has an area of 1.2 ha, where Santa Cruz giant waterlily (*Victoria cruziana*) and common waterlilies (*Nymphaea tetragona*) are cultivated.

Precious and Rare Tropical Plants

Mayodendron igneum.

Mayodendron igneum, a cauliflorous tree with edible flowers.

Santa Cruz giant waterlily (*Victoria cruziana*) flourishing in the open.

Legend has it that the Buddha Sakyamuni was born under one of these "carefree trees"(*Saraca declinata*),which are cauliflorous (bearing fruits on the trunk).

Sapria himalayana, a unique parasitic plant with giant flowers.

Konjak (*Amorphophalus virosus*) has flowers of about 20 cm in diameter.

Miraculous berry (*Synsepalum dulcificum*) with fruits that can temporarily change human's taste of sour foods to sweetness.

Cycas pectinata, a nationally-protected plant species, is grown in the Garden. These trees are several hundred years old.

Rambutan (*Nephelium lappaceum*) is a very valuable tropical fruit tree.

Lofty fig (*Ficus altissima*) produces aerial roots that look like stems, thus a single tree can grow into a forest .

Wine palm (*Borassus flabellifera*) introduced from Southeast Asia, produces fruits hanging in clusters.

Talipot palm (*Corypha umbraculifera*) grows vigorously. The leaves can be used to carve Buddhist Sutra on.

A nationally protected tree fern, *Alsophila spinulosa*.

A nationally protected staghorn fern, *Playcerium wallichii*.

The nationally protected feather tree (*Pellacalyx yunnanensis*) is a witness of the rapidly changing Garden.

Tacca chantrieri, a nationally protected plant with blue-purple flowers.

Xishuangbanna Tropical Botanical Garden

Public Education

The Visitors Service Centre has beautiful surroundings.

As one of the internationally renowned Botanical Gardens, the Garden receives thousands of foreign visitors every year.

Dunring the Water-Sprinkling Festival of the Dai Nationality, the local ethnic peoples are most interested in visiting the Garden of Ethnobotanical Culture.

Villages of Dai and other minority nationalities can be found near the Garden. They have unique cultures. This photo shows that the Dai monks are carving Buddhist Sutra on talipot palm (*Corypha umbraculifera*) leaves.

The Memorial Garden for late Prof. Tsai Hsetao, founder of the Botanical Garden, in which he planted a swordleaf dragon's blood tree (*Dracaena cochinchinensis*).

The Herbarium.

Co-operation and Exchanges

The participating botanists of the VI International Aroid Conference visit the Aroid Garden.

HRH The Prince Philip , Duke of Edinburgh of the United Kingdom, visits the Garden and plants a nationally protected tree, *Shorea chinensis,* for commemoration.

Chinese and German scientists on a joint survey of the tropical rain forest and ethnic culture.

Chinese and British scientists on a joint survey of the tropical rain forest.

The Garden is surrounded by the Luosuo River, a branch of the Mekong River.

A scene of great joy in the Luosuo River during Water-Sprinkling Festival of the Dai Nationlity.

THE CHINESE ACADEMY OF SCIENCES

KUNMING BOTANICAL GARDEN

Introduction

The Garden was founded in 1938, and is now affiliated to the Kunming Institute of Botany, Chinese Academy of Sciences. Prof. Tsai Hsetao, Prof. Wu Chengyih, Prof. Feng Kuomei and other prominent botanists contributed to its establishment and development. It is located in a famous scenic spot 12 km from the heart of Kunming City, at lat. 25° 01′ N, long. 102° 41′ E, and 1990 m above sea level, occupying 44 ha of land with 35 ha open to the public. The middle subtropical inland plateau climate is mild throughout the year, with an annual mean temperature of 14.7℃, mean daily temperature difference of 11.1℃, extreme maximum temperature of 31.5℃, extreme minimum temperate of − 5.4℃, mean annual precipitation of 1006.5 mm, mean relative humidity of 73%, and annual mean sunshine of 2470.3 hours.

The major tasks of the Garden are introduction and cultivation of ornamental plants, traditional Chinese medicinal plants, important trees and rare and endangered plants of Yunnan. Researches are focused on acclimatization and ex situ conservation of plant resources. The Garden is well maintained for research, public education, tourism and teaching, with the characteristics of Yunnan Province. Plants of nearly 4000 taxa are cultivated here. There are 10 specialized gardens, many experimental areas for plant introduction and cultivation, and 7 laboratories of cytogenetics, tissue culture, seed physiology, organic chemical analysis, soil analysis etc. The laboratories have 1500 m² floor area, and working rooms of 1000 m².

The Camellia Garden is 1 of the most distinctive specialized gardens that can be found in China; it features a collection of nearly 70 species of *Camellia*, 100 cultivars of *Camellia reticulata*, and many yellow camellias. The Rhododendron Garden has 320 species and cultivars mainly of evergreen rhododendrons. In the Magnolia Garden can be seen nearly 90 members of the Magnoliaceae. The Medicinal Herb Garden boasts 1000 species of plants which are used in traditional Chinese medicine. Trees and shrubs of 1170 species are in cultivation in the Arboretum. Some 380 taxa under national protection, such as *Davidia involucrata*, *Paeonia delavayi* var. *lutea* and *Paphiopedilum armeniacum*, are conserved ex situ in the Rare and Endangered Plants Section. The display glasshouses are decorated with 2000 species of tropical and subtropical plants.

The Garden has a staff of 75 people, among whom 55 are researchers and technicians, including 18 of senior rank and 14 of intermediate rank. Among the numerous research achievements, 14 have won prizes of the Chinese Academy of Sciences or at and above the provincial level. So far 110 papers and 13 books have been published; books like *Rhododendrons of China, Yunnan Camellias of China, Rare Flowers and Unusual Trees,* and *Orchids* have been very well received.

Academic exchanges and co-operative researches and expeditions have been undertaken with 150 botanical gardens and institutions of other countries. A twining relationship has been formed with the Royal Botanic Garden Edinburgh, UK. The Kunming Botanical Garden now receives 200 000 visitors a year, and enjoys a high reputation.

Add: Kunming Botanical Garden, Kunming Institute of Botany, Chinese Academy of Sciences,

    Heilongtan, North Suburb, Kunming, Yunnan 650204, China

Tel : (86-871) 5150660

Fax: (86-871) 5150227

Deng Xiaoping visiting the Kunming Botanical Garden (1962).

The Greenhouses

The greenhouses have 3000 m² of indoor area and 1.3 ha of outdoor area. There are the Succulent House, the South Subtropical Plant House, the Orchid House, the Shade Plant House, the Giant Waterlily House and outdoor flower beds, where more than 2000 species of tropical and subtropical plants are grown.

Cymbidium wenshanense, distributed in Wenshan of Yunnan, is a precious ornamental plant.

Fuli Gong, the complex of display greenhouses.

A *Vanda* hybrid.

The Orchid House. Orchids are 1 of the 8 famous flowers of Yunnan.

Cymbidium hookeranum var. *lowianum.*

Nymphaea alba in front of the Giant Waterlily House.

Phaius flavus, distributed in Yunnan, is a good indoor ornamental plant.

Argyroderma pearsonii, a native of South Africa, is an ornamental plant.

The Magnolia Garden

The Magnolia Garden has an area of 1.3 ha. More than 90 species belonging to 10 genera of the Magnoliaceae are grown in the Garden, one of the richest collection of the family in China. Nearly 60 species, including *Manglietia insignis, Magnolia delavayi* and *Michelia xanthantha*, have started to flower.

Magnolia delavayi.

Manglietia insignis, distributed in Yunnan, is used in gardens and as street trees.

A red form of *Magnolia delavayi,* distributed in Yunnan, is used in landscaping.

Michelia xanthantha, distributed in southeast Yunnan, has very ornamental flowers.

The entrance of the Magnolia Garden. Magnolias are 1 of the 8 famous flowers of Yunnan.

Kunming Botanical Garden

Rhododendron decorum.

The Rhododendron Garden

The Rhododendron Garden has an area of 2 ha, featuring high mountain evergreen rhododendrons, with around 320 species and cultivars, including *Rhodo-dend-ron giganteum* and *R. irror-atum* in the collection.

Rhododendron delavayi, distributed in Yunnan, Guizhou and other places, is for ornament and produces wood good for making handicrafts.

Rhododendron decorum, distributed in most parts of Yunnan, is for ornament.

The Rhododendron Garden. Rhododendrons are 1 of the 8 famous flowers of Yunnan.

Aresearcher hand-pollinates rhododendrons for crossbreeding.

The Camellia Garden

The Camellia Garden has an area of 2 ha. Around 40 species of the genus *Camellia*, including 11 species of yellow camellias, and more than 100 cultivars of *Camellia reticulata* and 300 cultivars of *Camellia japonica* are collected in the Garden, which is the earliest and the richest garden of *Camellia* species and cultivars in China.

Camellia reticulata 'Shizi Tou', a famous cultivar.

Camellia reticulata, distributed in Yunnan, is the city flower of Kunming.

Camellia nitidissima, distributed in Guangxi, is a rare species under national protection.

Camellia japonica 'Wucai'.

The Monument of Prof. Tsai Hsetao, founder of the Kunming Botanical Garden.

The Camellia Garden. Camellias are 1 of the 8 famous flowers of Yunnan.

Kunming Botanical Garden

The Rare and Endangered Plants Section

The Section has an area of 3.5 ha, conserving 380 species of rare and endangered plants. Many protected plants like *Davidia involucrata, Paeonia delavayi* var. *lutea* and *Paphiopedilum armeniacum* have started to flower.

Paeonia delavayi var. *lutea*.

Paphiopedilum armeniacum, distributed in west Yunnan, is a rare and endangered species under national protection.

Paeonia delavayi var. *lutea,* distributed in central, northwest and southwest Yunnan, is endemic to China and provides important genes for breeding yellow peony cultivars.

Trillium tschonoskii, distributed in Yunnan and Tibet, is used for ornament and medicine.

Amentotaxus yunnanensis, distributed in southeast Yunnan and southwest Guizhou, is a rare species with narrow range of distribution.

Kunming Botanical Garden

A view of the Gymnosperms Section.

The Gymnosperms Section

The Gymnosperms Section has an area of 2.3 ha. Nearly 200 species of Gymnosperms are collected here. Trees like *Taxus wallichiana, Pseudolarix amabilis, Fokienia hodginsii* and *Keteleeria evelyniana* are growing vigorously and have formed a unique landscape. The area is one of the beautiful scenic spots in the Garden.

Abies delavayi, distributed in northwest Yunnan, is good for timber and pulpwood.

Keteleeria evelyniana, distributed in most parts of Yunnan, produces wood for construction and furniture, seed oil for lubricating and for making soap, root bark for medicine.

Picea likiangensis, distributed in northwest Yunnan, is a fast-growing and high-quality timber tree good for afforestation.

The Arboretum

The Arboretum has an area of 23.5 ha. Around 1170 tree and shrub species in 411 genera and 130 families are collected here. Specialized areas for collections of the Rosaceae, Leguminosae and Hamamelidaceae have been established. The beautiful Sweetgum Walk has become a famous tourist spot in Kunming City.

Calycanthus floridus var. *ovatus,* introduced from North America, has beautiful flowers.

Sweetgum(*Liquidambar formosana*)*,* distributed in China from the west to Taiwan Province, is cultivated in gardens and as street trees.

Tripterygium hypoglaucum, distributed in Yunnan, produces beautiful fruits and the plant is also used medicinally.

Luculia intermedia, distributed in most parts of Yunnan and Tibet, has large inflorescences and fragrant flowers, and is a good landscape plant with great potential.

Kunming Botanical Garden

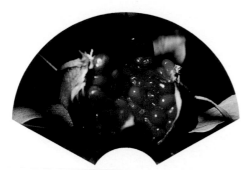

Paris polyphylla.

The Medicinal Herb Garden

The Medicinal Herb Garden has an area of 1.3 ha. More than 1000 species of medicinal plants, including some precious ones like *Panax notoginseng, Paris polyphylla* and *Aucklandia lappa,* are grown in the Garden.

Paris polyphylla, a medicinal plant.

Agastache rugosa, used as a medicine.

Ephedra likiangensis, distributed in northwest Yunnan, is used medicinally.

The Monocots Garden

The Monocots Garden has an area of 2 ha, with 200 species of mono-cotyledonous plants in cultivation. *Trachycarpus, Iris* and *Lilium* are well-represented and have formed an attractive landscape.

Nomocharis pardanthina, distributed in Yunnan, is an ornamental plant for gardens.

Lilium sargentiae, distributed in Yunnan, is an ornamental plant for gardens. Lilies (*Lilium*) are 1 of the 8 famous flowers of Yunnan.

Iris tectorum, a popular garden plant.

Musella lasiocarpa, endemic to Yunnan, is a plant for gardens. It is also used as forage and as a medicine.

The Alpine Plants Experimental Section

The Section has an area of 1 ha, where introduction, cultivation and breeding of alpine plants are conducted.

Meconopsis horridula var. *racemosa*. Blue poppies (*Meconopsis*) are 1 of the 8 famous flowers of Yunnan.

Incarvelia mairei, distributed in northwest Yunnan, is an alpine plant for gardens. Its fleshy root is used medicinally.

Primula vialii, distributed in northwest Yunnan, is an ornamental plant. Primroses (*Primula*) are 1 of the 8 famous flowers of Yunnan.

Joint field expedition of Chinese and foreign scientists.

Gentiana veitchiorum. Gentians (*Gentiana*) are 1 of the 8 famous flowers of Yunnan.

WUHAN BOTANICAL
GARDEN

Introduction

The Wuhan Botanical Garden is affiliated with the Wuhan Institute of Botany, Chinese Academy of Sciences. It is situated in the scenic area by the Donghu Lake, at the southern foot of Moshan Mountain, covering an area of 70 ha. The site is at lat. 30° 33′ N, long. 114° 24′ E, and 19–35 m above sea level, having a moist subtropical monsoon climate with annual mean temperature of 16.3°C, average minimum temperature of −3°C in January, extreme minimum temperature of −18.3°C, average maximum temperature of 35°C in July, extreme maximum temperature above 40°C, annual precipitation of 1282 mm, and mean relative humidity of 79%.

The Garden was founded in 1956. Among the 60 staff members whom are 21 senior and 11 intermediate researchers and technicians. Well-known botanists Prof. Chung Hsinhsuan, Prof. Zhang Wencai, Prof. Chen Fenghwai, Prof. Sun Hsiangchung and the staff members made great contributions to the establishment and development of the Garden through their pioneering hard work.

Researches are carried out on introduction, acclimatization, breeding, propagation, cultivation, ex situ conservation and utilization of resource plants of Central China and aquatic plants from inland waters of the whole country, based on floristic studies. Among the 37 important research projects accomplished, 12 have been awarded with prizes at or above provincial and ministerial level. Other achievements include 13 books, 168 papers, breeding of more than 10 high-yielding quality cultivars of economic plants, and development of medicine, health food, antimould agent, essence, perfume, environmentally friendly pesticide, and fruit preservative.

The Botanical Garden has constructed more than 10 specialized gardens and landscaped areas, such as the Ornamental Plants Section, the Actinidia Garden, the Arboretum, the Medicinal Plants Garden, the Rare and Endangered Plants Section, the Bamboo Garden by the lakeside, the Central Lawn and the Aquatic Plants Section, featuring diverse taxa, shapes and colours. Nearly 4000 taxa of plants are cultivated here, making the Garden the largest centre for preservation of plant germplasm resources and base for conservation of plant diversity in Central China.

In recent years co-operation with Chinese and foreign institutions has been further strengthened, involving long-term seed exchange with botanical gardens and arboreta in 44 countries and regions, and collaboration in research, training and cultural exchange with over 30 countries and regions, such as the construction of the Chinese Lotus Garden in California, USA, the kiwifruit project in collaboration with New Zealand, and the study in collaboration with Gifu Pharmaceutical University, Japan, on medicinal plants described in *Materia Medica* written by the renowned Chinese herbalist Li Shizhen of the Ming Dynasty.

The Garden receives each year 50 000 visitors, including college students and schoolchildren. The extension of research achievements, technical consultation and training, production and sale of economic and ornamental plants, and landscape design and planting have created marked economic and social benefits.

Add: Wuhan Botanical Garden, Wuhan Institute of Botany, Chinese Academy of Sciences,

Moshan, Wuchang District, Wuhan, Hubei 430074, China

Tel : (86-27) 7409218

Fax: (86-27) 7801251

The Lotus Pond.

The Aquatic Plants Section

The Section covers an area of 4 ha, and consists of a man-made river, a lotus and waterlily display area, a germplasm resource plot and an ecological experimental area for aquatic plants. More than 40 waterlily cultivars, 160 lotus cultivars and 300 species of other aquatic plants are cultivated in the Section, forming the richest collection of aquatic plants in China.

The pavilion in the lake of the Aquatic Garden.

Sacred lotus (*Nelumbo nucifera*) 'Bingdi', a rare cultivar with 2 flower buds on 1 scape or 2 ovaries in 1 flower, which is a symbol of love.

Sacred lotus (*Nelumbo nucifera*) 'Sino-Japanese Friendship', a hybrid bred in the Wuhan Botanical Garden in 1965 by crossing 'Chinese Ancient' lotus (the male parent, grown from unearthed seed of over 1000 years ago in Pulandian, Liaoning Province, China) with 'Ohga' lotus (the female parent, grown from unearthed seed of over 2000 years ago in Chiba Prefecture, Japan).

Sacred lotus (*Nelumbo nucifera*) 'Hong Qian Ye', a precious cultivar with up to 1000 red petals, most of which are modified stamens.

Sacred lotus (*Nelumbo nucifera*) 'Bai Qian Ye', a precious cultivar with up to 1000 white petals, most of which are modified stamens.

The Garden-in-the-Garden.

Iris wilsonii, a bog plant.

The Lotus Pond.

The landscape of the Wuhan Botanical Garden.

Sactred lotus (*Nelumbo nucifera*) 'Shouxing Tao'.

Sinojackia xylocarpa.

The Rare and Endangered Plants Section

The Section covers an area of 2 ha, with 130 nationally protected species cultivated here. Some of them, such as *Metasequoia glyptostroboides, Taiwania flousiana, Pseudolarix kaempferi, Eurycorymbus cavaleriei, Sinojackia xylocarpa, Zenia insignis, Cercidiphyllum japonicum, Tapiscia sinensis, Pterostyrax psilophylla, Liriodendron chinense, Ormosia hosiei* and *Corylus chinensis,* have formed forests;many others, such as *Davidia involucrata, Pseudotsuga sinensis, Abies chensiensis, Stewartia sinensis, Calycanthus chinensis* and *Manglietia patungensis,* are also flourishing.

Sinojackia xylocarpa, a rare tree species endemic to China.

Pseudolarix amabilis among the trees is like the rare and precious giant panda among the animals.

Corylus chinensis, a woody species endemic to China.

Ormosia henryi, a famous tree for wood carving.

Eurycorymbus cavaleriei, the only species of the genus, is endemic to China.

Taiwania flousiana, a relict plant endemic to China.

Zenia insignis, the only species of the genus, is endemic to China.

Actinidia.

The Actinidia Garden

The Garden covers an area of 3.5 ha. Nearly 40 species and over 160 cultivars and strains of *Actinidia* are grown here, forming the largest *Actinidia* germplasm resource bank in China. Many fine cultivars bred in the Garden, such as 'Wuzhi 2', 'Wuzhi 3', 'Wuzhi 5', 'Tongshan 5' and 'Jianhong 1', rival New Zealand's kiwifruit cultivar 'Hayward' in yield, fruit weight and other qualities.

Actinidia eriantha.

The fruit of a fine *Actinidia* cultivar 'Wuzhi 3'.

A panorama of the Actinidia Garden.

The Medicinal Plants Garden

The Garden covers an area of 2.5 ha, with over 800 species of medicinal plants introduced and cultivated. It is one of the largest medicinal plants garden in China. Precious medicinal plants from the Qinling-Bashan Mountains and Wuling Mountains, especially from the Shennongjia Mountains, such as *Dendrobium hancockii*, *Paris polyphylla* var. *stenophylla* , *Dysosma versipellis*, *Saruma henryi*, *Taxus chinensis*, *Coptis chinensis*, *Eucommia ulmoides*, *Magnolia officinalis*, can be seen here.

Codonopsis lanceolata, a tonic medicinal herb.

A corner of the shelter for medicinal shade plants.

Wuhan Botanical Garden

Medicinal Plants *pachysandra terminalis* and *Reineckia carnea*.

The inauguration ceremony for the statue of the great herbalist Li Shizhen.

Paris polyphylla var. *stenophylla*, an antidote to snake venom.

Dendrobium hancockii, a medicinal herb.

The Ornamental Plants Section

The Section covers an area of 3 ha, consisting of the Display Greenhouses, the Rose Garden, the Rhododendron Garden, the Tree Peony Garden, the Camellia Garden, the Herbaceous Flowers Garden and the Shade Plants Garden. Over 1200 species and cultivars are grown here, featuring tree peonies (200 cultivars) from the north, tropical and subtropical ornamental plants (400 taxa) from the south, and shade ferns (100 taxa) from high mountains.

Rhododendron simsii.

Dicentra spectabilis, a traditional flower in China.

Echinocactus grusonii, a desert plant.

Narcissus jonquilla.

The Succulent House.

The Bamboo Gardern.

The Bamboo Garden

The Garden covers an area of 2.5 ha, with over 100 species of bamboos mostly ornamental, such as *Bambusa ventricosa, Bambusa glaucescens, Phyllostachys aurea, Bambusa emeiensis, Phyllostachys bambusoides, Chimonobambusa quadrangularis, Bambusa vulgaris* and *Phyllostachys viridis*. The Jun An Pavilion of imitated bamboo structure was built in the Garden.

Bambusa glaucescens, a famous oramental bamboo.

Bambusa chungii, a tall and handsome bamboo.

The Gymnosperms Section

The Section covers an area of 7 ha, with 110 species of gymnosperms introduced from China and abroad. Some of the more precious and important species include *Metasequoia glyptostroboides, Cathaya argyrophylla, Glyptostrobus pensilis, Fokienia hodginsii, Sabina chinensis, Cedrus deodara, Taxus chinensis, Cunninghamia unicanaliculata, Picea wilsonii, Cryptomeria fortunei, Keteleeria davidiana, Pinus elliottii, Sabina chinensis* 'Pyramidalis', *Sabina virginiana, Taxodium ascendens* and *Cephalotaxus oliveri.*

Taxodium ascendens.

Pond cypress (*Taxodium ascendens*) forming a forest in wetland.

Cryptomeria fortunei, a good timber tree.

Sabina chinensis, a landscape tree.

The Pinetum.

Wuhan Botanical Garden

Autumn scenery in the Maple Garden.

The Arboretum

The Arboretum covers an area of 10 ha, with more than 800 species of broad-leaved woody plants of 60 families. Well-represented are the Magnoliaceae, Ulmaceae, Fagaceae, Lauraceae, Rosaceae, Leguminosae, Celastraceae, Aquifoliaceae, Theaceae, Aceraceae, Oleaceae, Ericaceae and Caprifoliaceae.

The Peach Blossom Garden.

The Fugu Pavilion in spring.

The Yunjin Bridge.

A snow scene of the Friendship Pavilion.

The Wengcui Pavilion.

Students visit the greenhouse.

Students are attracted by the science boards.

LUSHAN
BOTANICAL GARDEN

Introduction

The Lushan Botanical Garden is under the dual leadership of Jiangxi Province and the Chinese Academy of Sciences. The central area of the Garden is located in the valley of Hanpokou, southeast of the Mount Lushan, Jiangxi Province, at lat. 29° 35′ N, Long. 115° 59′ E, and 1000—1300 m above sea level. The site has an undulate topography, with yellow-brown soil of 5.0—6.5pH. It has a subtropical eastern moist monsoon montane climate, with annual mean temperature of 12.3℃, extreme maximum temperature of 30.3℃, extreme minimum temperature of −16.8℃, average 193 foggy days a year, annual precipitation of 1800—2000 mm, and mean relative humidity of 79.7%.

The Botanical Garden was founded in 1934, formerly called the Lushan Forest Botanical Garden. The founders included famous Chinese botanists Prof. Hu Hsenhsu, Prof. Ching Renchang and Prof. Chen Fenghwai. The Garden is an important base of plant introduction, acclimatization, conservation, wild plant resource utilization and public education.

Occupying nearly 300 ha of land and holding a living collection of 3400 plant taxa, the Garden contains the Coniferous Section, the International Friendship Rhododendron Garden, the Greenhouse Section, the Herbaceous Section, the Arboretum, the Rock Garden, the Actinidia Garden, the Medicinal Herb Garden, and the Tea Plantation. The Arboretum holds a collection of more than 300 *Rhododendron* species from home and abroad, with the peak blooming season in May. The Lushan mist tea produced here is renowned in China and around the world. The Medicinal Herb Garden has more than 300 species of medicinal plants in cultivation. In the Coniferous Section there are over 260 species of gymnosperms, including the "living fossil"——*Metasequoia glyptostroboides*, the Chinese endemic *Pseudolarix amabilis*, and other noble and valuable trees. The Herbarium has 170 000 specimens, and the Library holds more than 60 000 books.

In the last 20 years, 59 research programmes have been undertaken, with 13 scientific and technological achievements being made, the major ones of which include volume 1 of the *Flora of Jiangxi Province*; the introduction and acclimatization of *Abies firma, Cryptomeria fortunei, Chamaecyparis obtusa, C. pisifera* and *Thuja occidentalis*; the study on techniques of experimental plant taxonomy; the study on moths of Mount Lushan; and the breeding of *Actinidia chinensis* '79-2'. Six books and over 600 scientific papers have been published.

The Garden now has a staff of 116, including 47 researchers and technicians, of which 10 are of senior rank, 13 of intermediate rank and 24 of junior rank. Seed exchange and academic contacts are made with 270 institutions in 68 countries. The Garden is a member of the IUCN. Each year, 20 000 foreign guests, Chinese students and professionals come to visit, investigate or have practice, and 60 000 tourists are received here. Sales of trees, flowers and the Lushan mist tea are conducted. The Garden also actively contributes to the efforts of making urban environments beautiful, green and fragrant, and of helping the economic development of poor areas. The Garden is elaborating on its master plan, emphasizing its key aspects and strengthening its special features to combine studies on biodiversity conservation with rapid construction of the garden landscape, in developing the Garden into a subalpine botanical garden of advanced international standard.

Add: Lushan Botanical Garden, Jiangxi Province and Chinese Academy of Sciences,

    Hanpokou, Lushan, Jiangxi 332900, China

Tel : (86-792) 8282542, (86-792) 8281678

Fax: (86-792) 8282223

Lushan Botanical Garden

Sciadopitys verticillata, 1 of the 3 most popular garden trees in the world.

The Coniferous Section

This Section has an area of 2 ha. Through our 60 years' efforts, 250 species of coniferous trees belonging to 41 genera and 11 families have been successfully introduced from China and the world. The Botanical Garden is therefore praised as a living specimen garden of conifers.

Abies firma.

Taxus chinensis var. *mairei.*

Pseudolarix amabilis.

The Arboretum

The Arboretum covers an area of 1.3 ha. Over 300 species of broad-leaved trees and shrubs mainly introduced from the middle and lower reach of the Changjiang River are grown here. They belong to 76 families and include many Chinese endemic, rare and endangered plants with high scientific, economic and ornamental values, such as *Bretschneidera sinensis, Davidia involucrata, Cercidiphyllum japonicum, Tapiscia sinensis* and *Emmenopterys henryi.*

A view of the Arboretum.

Magnolia sieboldii, under national protection.

Magnolia officinalis subsp. *biloba.*

Tapiscia sinensis, under national protection.

Liriodendron chinense.

Calanthe sp.

The Rock Garden

The Rock Garden simulates nature with rocks piled against small hills and plants cultivated among stones. Through many years' introduction, alpine plants such as gentians (*Gentiana*), primroses (*Primula*), pinks (*Dianthus*) and rhododendrons have formed attractive natural scenes.

Cypripedium japonicum.

A path winding in the Rock Garden.

Primula sp.

The International Friendship Rhododendron Garden

Rhododendrons are one of the major flowers introduced from home and abroad and cultivated in the Botanical Garden. The number of species has reached 300 and in early May the rhododendron flowers are colourful and spectacular.

Rhododendron mariae.

Rhododendron kiangsiense.

Rhododendron fortunei.

Rhododendron liliiflorum.

A red form of *Rhododendron molle* cultivar.

Lushan Botanical Garden

Ardisia mamillata.

The Greenhouses

Displayed in the Greenhouses are 600 taxa of rare and precious flowers such as begonias and fuchsias, and tropical and subtropical succulents. The total area is 1700 m², with cool houses included.

The Succulent collection.

Ardisia mamillata.

Sinningia hybrida.

Abutilon striatum.

Crinum moorei.

GUILIN
BOTANICAL GARDEN

Introduction

The Guilin Botanical Garden is affiliated to the Guangxi Guilin Institute of Botany, Guangxi Zhuang Autonomous Region and Chinese Academy of Sciences. It is situated in Yanshan Town, Guilin City, Guangxi Zhuang Autonomous Region, at lat. 25° 01′ N, long. 110° 17′ E, and 180 −1300 m above sea level, having a subtropical monsoon climate, with annual mean temperature of 18.8℃, extreme maximum temperature of 38℃, extreme minimum temperature of − 3.3℃, and annual precipitation of 1800 mm. The Botanical Garden was founded in 1958, with famous botanists Prof. Chun Woonyoung and Prof. Tsoong Chihsin as its founders and for a long time its leaders. It aims at collecting mainly southern subtropical plants, with emphasis on Guangxi and limestone endemics, rare and endangered plants, and diverse economic and ornamental plants.

The Garden has an area of 67 ha, with a collection of 2100 plant taxa, including 181 nationally protected species. The Gymnosperms Section, the Palm and Cycad Section, the Medicinal Plants Section, the Flower and Penjing Garden, the Rare and Endangered Plants Garden, and the Magnolia Garden have been established for display. The Gingko Elite Garden, the Actinidia Germplasm Resources Plot and High-yield Demonstration Garden, the Yellow Camellia Germplasm Resources Plot, and the Chinese Tallow Tree Cultivar Garden have rich germplasm resources in stock. Specialized gardens of rhododendrons, orchids, sweet osmanthus, bamboos and aquatic plants are planned for construction. The luxuriant trees and flowers and the ideal position on the popular tourist route between Guilin and Yangshuo have makes the Garden a favourite tourist resort.

Multidisciplinary studies were conducted on plants such as *Siraitia grosvenori, Ginkgo biloba, Actinidia* species, yellow *Camellia* species, *Sapium sebiferum,* and *Ilex kudingcha* subsp. *pruniflorum,* which greatly contributed to the economic development of Guangxi. Through the years, 215 scientific results were achieved, 47 of which were rewarded with scientific and technological prizes, including 16 provincial and ministerial prizes. Part of the compilation work of the books *Vegetation of China* and *Flora of China* were undertaken by botanists in the Garden. Other special books written and produced here include *List of Guangxi Plants; Flora of Guangxi* Vol. 1; *Guangxi Medicinal Plants Used in Traditional Chinese Veterinary Medicine; Atlas of Limestone Mountain Plants of Guangxi; Rhododendrons of Huaping, Guangxi.* The Herbarium houses 300 000 sheets of plant specimens. The Library has 60 000 books and 20 000 volumes of 1000 periodicals.

The staff has 264 members, among whom 162 are researchers and technicians, including 61 of senior rank, 58 of intermediate rank and 43 of junior rank.

The Guilin Botanical Garden has had friendly academic exchanges with many Chinese and foreign botanical gardens and research institutions. Seventeen staff members have been to other countries for short visits or further studies; 238 foreign specialists have been received in the Garden; seed and other material exchanges are made with over 20 countries. The Garden is further broadening the fields of co-operation and drawing investment from various parties, in its effort to speed up the construction and to improve the overall function of the Garden.

Add: Guilin Botanical Garden, Guangxi Zhuang Autonomous Region and Chinese Academy of Sciences,

Yanshan, Guilin, Guangxi Zhuang Autonomous Region 541006, China

Tel : (86-773) 3550194

Fax: (86-773) 3550067

The Flower and Penjing (Miniature Landscape) Garden

Covering an area of 2 ha, the Garden has more than 300 taxa of trees for penjing (miniature landscapes) and flowers. It is a major display area for ornamental plants, including penjing of *Lagerstroemia guilinensis* and *Podocarpus macrophyllus*, and precious flowers of orchids, *Zantedeschia aethiopica* and *Epipremnum aureum*.

Yellow camellia (*Camellia nitidissima*).

Red orchid cactus (× *Heliochia* 'Ackermannii') has high ornamental value and medicinal uses.

Zantedeschia aethiopica with flowers of 7 different colours , was introduced from New Zealand.

Osmanthus fragrans, a famous flowering shrub, blooms in September with intense fragrance. It has been chosen as the city flower of Guilin.

Yellow camellia (*Camellia nitidissima*), a precious rare plant endemic to Guangxi, bears bright golden-yellow flowers in leaf axils in early spring.

China rose (*Rosa hybrida*), whose blossoms are very colourful and have delicate fragrance, is often planted in gardens.

The Palm and Cycad Section

The Section occupies an area of 1 ha, with 31 species of palms and 7 species of cycads in the collection. Representative plants are *Guihaia argyrata, Caryota urens, Cycas micholitzii* and *Cycas pectinata.*

The Magnolia Garden

The Garden occupies an area of 1.3 ha, with 105 species of the Magnoliaceae, including 20 rare and endangered species. It is an important base for scientific researches. Representative plants are *Kmeria septentrionalis, Manglietia sinoconifera* and *Michelia hedyosperma.*

The wine palm (*Caryota urens*) is a rare large ornamental palm for tropical and subtropical regions.

Manglietia sinoconifera, distributed in Napo County of Guangxi, blooms in June.

Cycas micholitzii, a rare and endangered species distributed in Longzhou County of Guangxi (left: male, right: female).

Deutzianthus tonkinensis.

The Rare and Endangered Plants Garden

The Garden occupies an area of 1.33 ha, conserving 181 taxa under national protection, among which 129 are from Guangxi, and 54 are calciphiles (lime-loving plants). Representative species are *Cathaya argyrophylla*, *Parashorea chinensis*, *Deutzianthus tonkinensis* and *Burretiodendron hsienmu.*

Yellow-branchlet Keteleeria (*Keteleeria calecarea*).

Cathaya argyrophylla, a relict plant highly valuable for scientific research.

Rauwolfia verticillata is distributed in Guangxi, Guangdong, Yunnan and Guizhou. Its roots contain alkaloids and are used for treatment of hypertension and also used by local people for treatment of fever caused by influenza, insomnia and dizziness.

The Medicinal Plants Section

The Section occupies an area of 3 ha, with more than 800 taxa of medicinal plants, including trees, shrubs, herbs and climbers. Many of them are endemic to Guangxi, giving the display area a unique feature. Representative plants include precious Chinese medicinal herbs such as *Amomum villosum, Cinnamomum cassia, Illicium difengpi*, and important medicinal plants such as *Taxus chinensis* and *Cratoxylum formosum* subsp. *pruniflorum*.

Aristolochia fangchi is a medicinal plant occurring mainly in Guangxi. Its roots are used to treat rheumatism and its fruits are effective in relieving cough.

Ipomoea turbinata, often cultivated, is used locally for treatment of injuries. It grows wild in southern Yunnan.

Excoecaria venenata, growing on limestone hills, is endemic to Guangxi. It is used for treatment of dermatitis.

The Shade Plants Section	**The Economic Plants Section**
The Section occupies an area of 3 ha, is an attractive spot for visitors. About 600 taxa of trees, shrubs, herbaceous and climbing plants, including ornamental, aromatic and oil plants, are cultivated in this Section.	The Section occupies an area of 5 ha, with 75 *Actinidia* taxa, 34 *Ginkgo biloba* cultivars and 35 *Sapium sebiferum* cultivars, as well as many other fine economic plants, including *Siraitia grosvenori* and large-fruited seedless wampee (*Clausena lansium*).

A view of the Shade Plants Section.

Ginkgo biloba 'Guilin 86-1', early-maturing with high-yield.

Chirita gueilinensis, growing on limestone hills of Guilin, has many beautiful flowers.

Siraitia grosvenori, a famous economic plant endemic to Guangxi.

DINGHUSHAN ARBORETUM

Introduction

The Dinghushan Arboretum is affiliated to the South China Institute of Botany, Chinese Academy of Sciences, and is located in Dinghu Mountain, Zhaoqing City, Guangdong Province, 86 km west of Guangzhou and 19 km east of Zhaoqing. The site is at lat. 23° 10′ N, long. 112° 34′ E, and 14.1–1000.3 m above sea level, having red, yellow and mountain shrub-meadow soils. The southern subtropical monsoon moist climate here has annual mean temperature of 20.9℃, average temperature of 28.1℃ in July, average temperature of 12.0℃ with occasional frost in January, extreme minimum temperature of − 0.2℃, annual precipitation of 1956 mm, and mean relative humidity of 81.5%. The wet season, lasting from April to September, is clearly demarcated from the dry season from October to March.

The Arboretum was founded in 1956, with the initiative and efforts of Prof.Chien Sungshu, Prof. Yang Weiyi, Prof. Ching Renchang, Prof. Chun Woonyoung and others, for purposes of monitoring and studying the plants and their environments in Dinghu Mountain, of collecting and conserving the plant germplasm resources, of introduction, acclimatization and extension of superior useful plants and rare and precious plants. The Arboretum is in charge of the management of the Dinghushan National Nature Reserve, and the 2 together with the later-estabished Dinghushan Forest Ecosystem Research Station form a single unit.

The mountains here are towering high, covered with green forests of tall old trees, decorated with water falls and streams, with birds singing and flowers giving off their fragrance. Within the 1133 ha of the Arboretum can be found 1843 taxa of wild higher plants and 673 taxa of cultivated plants. The combined beauty of the primitive natural setting and the modern landscape architecture are best embodied by the Dinghushan Rare and Endangered Plants Garden, the South China Rhododendron Garden, the Precious Ornamental Plants Garden and the Bamboo Garden, where diverse plants are flourishing. Rare and endangered plants are conserved in situ (22 species) and ex situ (74 species) in the Arboretum; 6 of the species have been propagated in large quantities and reintroduced to natural habitats, and trees of *Podocarpus fleuryi* have been so widely planted that the species features the roads in Dinghu Mountain. Three permanent forest plots are designated for monitoring the dynamics of biodiversity. The Herbarium has accumulated more than 18 000 sheets of plant specimens.

There are currently 24 people working in the Arboretum, including 3 senior and 2 intermediate researchers and technicians. Three books, 7 volumes of *Studies on Tropical and Subtropical Forest Ecosystems* (special collections of papers) and 200 papers reporting achievements of researches conducted here have been published. Each year, over 100 foreign scholars come to visit and investigate in the Arboretum, more than 500 college students and schoolchildren come here for practice or for activities of summer and winter camps, and the number of tourists amount to 500 000 – 600 000.

Add: Dinghushan Arboretum, South China Institute of Botany, Chinese Academy of Sciences,

Dinghushan,Zhaoqing, Guangdong 526070, China

Tel : (86 - 758) 2621116

Fax: (86 - 758) 2623242

Dinghushan Arboretum

Collecting specimens.

The iron tower for scientific observation.

The forest for sight-seeing.

The waterfall above the Feishui Tan Pool.

The Double-Rainbow Bridge.

Landscape in the Arboretum.

A corner of the Bamboo Garden.

Flower production in the nursery.

Flower production

Rhodomyrtus tomentosa, a wild flower.

Ficus microcarpa.

Ficus hispida, a cauliflorous plant.

An elegant tree fern *(Alsophila podophylla).*

An old tree of *Canarium album.*

Dinghushan Arboretum

Alsophila spinulosa, a nationally protected plant.

The Rare and Endangered Plants Garden

The Rare and Endangered Plants Garden covers an area of 2 ha and holds 74 species listed in the first list of nationally protected plants. *Alsophila spinulosa*, under national protection is among them.

Nageia fleuryi, a nationally protected plant.

Cycas taiwaniana, a nationally protected plant.

Tsoongiodendron odorum, a nationally protected plant.

Erythrophleum fordii, a nationally protected plant.

The Dinghushan Precious Ornamental Plants Garden

The Dinghushan Precious Ornamental Plants Garden covers an area of 0.7 ha, holding 168 species of epiphytic, shade, medicinal, rare and ornametal plants, including *Begonia fimbristipula*, *Drynaria fortunei* and *Clematis filamentosa*.

Rhododendron mariae.

Rhododendron mariae.

Begonia fimbristipula, source of the well-known begonia tea of Dinghushan.

Drynaria fortunei, a medicinal plant.

126

TURPAN EREMOPHYTES
BOTANICAL GARDEN

Introduction

This Garden is affiliated to the Xinjiang Institute of Biology, Pedology and Desert Research, Chinese Academy of Sciences, and forms a unit with the Turpan Desert Research Station of the same Institute. Located 10 km southeast of the City of Turpan in Xinjiang Uygur Autonomous Region, at lat. 40° 51′ N, long. 89° 11′ E, and 95 − 76 m below sea level, it is the botanical garden in the world with the lowest elevation. The place has a warm temperate continental desert climate, with annual mean temperature of 13.9℃, extreme maximum temperature of 47.6℃ —— the highest in China (the highest temperature on sand surface exceeding 80 ℃ in summer), extreme minimum temperature of −28℃, annual precipitation of 16.4 mm, and mean relative humidity of 41.0%.

The Garden was founded in 1976, and its work is directed to ex situ preservation of germplasm resources of plants from arid and desert areas and conservation of eremophytes diversity. The research programmes place emphasis on the introduction and acclimatization, ecology, biology and physiological characteristics of eremophytes, the conservation of rare and endangered desert plants, the selection and cultivation techniques of good sand-fixing plants.

The Garden occupies 34 ha of land, with 463 taxa of desert plants belonging to 247 genera and 72 families, including 43 species of rare and endangered plants introduced into cultivation. Specialty collections can be found in the Taxonomic Garden of Eremophytes, the Tamaricaceous Garden, which holds nearly 20 species— over half of the total number of the species of the Tamaricaceae family in China, and the Ethnic Medicinal Herb Garden with over 50 species of medicinal plants, mainly those commonly used by the Uygur people. Areas for collections of rare and endangered eremophytes, wild flowers and aromatic plants from the desert, and precious ornamental trees will be established. Research facilities include the Living Plants Laboratory, the Laboratory of Plant Morphology and Anatomy, the Laboratory of Plant Physiology, the Herbarium and the Information Section. There are also a nursery, an orchard area and an automatic meteorological observational site in the Garden.

The staff numbers 12, of whom 5 are researchers and technicians. Since the foundation of the Garden, 9 research achievements have been awarded with national, provincial or ministerial prizes. The major achievements include researches on large area sand-fixation and afforestation in Turpan; introduction, stock raising and afforestation of tamarisks; introduction and acclimatization of fine sand-fixing plants; *Capparis spinosa* and techniques for its cultivation; biological characteristics of *Glycyrrhiza uralensis* and techniques for its cultivation; introduction and characteristics of rare and endangered desert plants of Xinjiang. Two books and over 100 papers have been published.

The Garden area joins the large expanse of sand-fixing vegetation, which facilitates the combination of desert research, control and utilization. The Garden has been designated as a new tourist scenic spot, where what was formerly barren wind-eroded shifting sands is now covered with vigorously growing vegetation. It also has become a teaching and practice base for college and polytechnic school students, and so far has received over 20 000 domestic professional and touring visitors, teachers and schoolchildren, as well as nearly 1000 scholars from some 20 countries. Two projects in collaboration with Japan are in progress. Good conditions for international co-operation is provided by the newly-constructed apartment houses for visiting specialists.

Add: Turpan Eremophytes Botanical Garden, Xinjiang Institute of Biology, Pedology and Desert Research,

Chinese Academy of Sciences, Qiatkale Township, Turpan, Xinjiag 838008, China

Tel : (86-991) 3835294 (Institute), (86-995) 524643 (Garden)

Fax: (86-991) 3835459 (Institute)

Turpan Eremophytes Botanical Garden

Successful greening and cultivation of melons and vegetables deep in Taklimakan Desert.

The automatic meteorological station.

A summer camp evening by bonfire.

Passing on techniques of controlling moving sands.

College students doing practice in the Botanical Garden.

Providing seed of good sand-fixing plants to desert regions.

The Systematic Garden of Eremophytes

Founded in 1976, the Garden occupies an area of 8 ha. Over 400 species of eremophytes belonging to 200 genera of 60 families are introduced and cultivated here. Among them are 43 rare and endangered species, most of which are under 2nd or 3rd degree national protection. Taxa with distinct features for desert habitat include *Tamarix, Calligonum, Ammopiptanthus, Nitraria, Glycyrrhiza* and *Haloxylon.* The number of species accounts for over 80% of the total number of desert plants in China. Growing in the Garden, they form the characteristic landscape of arid land and desert.

Atraphaxis bracteata, a good sand-fixing pioneer shrub, grows in drift sand, and can be used as a fodder. It is endemic to Ordos and Alxa in Inner Mongolia.

Ammopiptanthus nanus, a nationally protected relic species used for ornament and afforestation, is distributed only in the arid low mountain region in southern Xinjiang in China and in small amount in neighbouring countries.

Calligonum junceum, a good sand-fixing and ornamental shrub, occurs in gravel desert, sands and fixed sand dunes in Xinjiang, Inner Mongolia, Mongolia and Middle Asia.

Hexinia polydichotoma, a perennial herb , is the only species of *Hexinia* of the Asteraceae. It is endemic to China, distributed in Gansu and Xinjiang. The plant has ornamental value and can be used for sand-fixation.

Gymnocarpos przewalskii, a nationally protected plant, occurs on gravel hillsides in deserts in Xinjiang, Gansu, Ningxia, Qinghai and Inner Mongolia of China.

Calligonum rubicundum, a good sand-fixing and ornamental shrub, is distributed in Xinjiang of China and in Kazakhstan.

Apocynum venetum, a perennial herb, occurs in river banks in deserts in northwestern China and in Middle Asia. It is used for ornament, fodder, medicine and fibre material.

Populus euphratica, a nationally protected plant, is one of the major edificators in deserts of China and a salt- and alkali-tolerant tree for shelter-forests. The species occurs in the desert of Xinjiang, Gansu and Inner Mongolia, and is distributed in both Asia and Africa.

The Tamaricaceous Garden

Founded in 1992, it covers an area of 8 ha, with 17 species of the Tamaricaceae planted, amounting to 50% of the total species of the family. The Tamaricaceae assume a dominant position in deserts of China, with the genus *Tamarix* being highly valuable for sand fixation, ornament, fodder, weaving material and firewood.

Tamarix hispida, a shrub, occurs in desert regions in China, Mongolia and Middle Asia. It is ornamental and good for sand fixation in salinized sandy lands, and also produces fodder, weaving material and firewood.

Tamarix laxa, a shrub, occurs in desert regions in China, Mongolia and Middle Asia. It is ornamental and good for sand fixation in salinized sandy lands, and also produces fodder, weaving material and firewood.

Tamarix androssowii, a shrub, occurs in desert regions in China, Mongolia and Middle Asia. It is ornamental and good for sand fixation in salinized sandy lands, and also produces fodder, weaving material and firewood.

Tamarix elongata, a shrub, occurs in desert regions in China, Mongolia and Middle Asia. It is ornamental and good for sand fixation in salinized sandy lands, and also produces fodder, weaving material and firewood.

Turpan Eremophytes Botanical Garden

Allium mongolicum occurs in fixed sands, low mountain slopes and dry riverbeds in desert and semi-desert regions in northwest China. It is used as medicine, fodder and food.

The Ethnic Medicinal Herb Garden

Founded in 1992, it occupies an area of 0.5 ha. Over 50 species of medicinal herbs commonly used by Uygur, Kazakh, Mongolian and some other ethnic groups are in the collection, with emphasis on desert species. In addition to medicinal use, many plants are valuable as sources of food, fodder, spices or for ornament. The Garden is one of the senic spots of the Turpan Erem-ophytes Botanical Garden.

Nitraria tangutorum, a good sand-fixing shrub, occurs in sandy soil and clay soil in deserts and semi-deserts in western China. It is used as fodder, medicine and food.

Cistanche tubulosa, a nationally protected species, is a perennial medicinal plant parasitic on roots of various species of *Tamarix*. It is distributed in southern Xinjiang in China and also in Middle and West Asia and North Africa.

Glycyrrhiza inflata, a perennial herb, occurs in sandy saline grasslands or river bank forests of deserts in China, Middle Asia and Mongolia. It is used for medicine, fodder or spice.

Hedysarum scoparium.

Poacynum pictum.

Ammopiptanthus mongolicus.

Caragana intermedia.

SHENYANG ARBORETUM

Introduction

The Shenyang Arboretum, affiliated with the Institute of Applied Ecology, Chinese Academy of Sciences, is located in the middle section of the beautifully-landscaped South Canal Belt Park in Shenyang City, at lat. 41° 46′ N, long. 123° 26′ E, and 41.6 m above sea level, on a flat land with deep fertile forest soil of 7 pH. The warm temperate semi-moist monsoon continental climate features distinct four seasons and simultaneous rain and heat in summer, and has annual mean temperature of 7.4℃, extreme maximum temperature of 38.3℃, extreme minimum temperature of − 30.5℃, and annual precipitation of 755.4 mm.

The Arboretum was originally called Botanical Garden when established in 1955 under the direction of prominent botanist Prof. Liou Tchenngo and forest scientist and ecologist Prof. Wang Chan, but adopted the present name in 1977. Its major tasks involve the introduction of trees from northern China, systematic studies on the Salicaceae, *Picea* of the Pinaceae and non-leguminous nitrogen-fixing tree species, as well as the introduction and acclimatization of precious trees of Chinese and foreign origins. It has become 1 of the centres where germplasm resources of wild plants are preserved. On its 5 ha of land are planted nearly 450 taxa of trees and shrubs, arranged by families and genera, including 50 species from abroad and 25 species protected at the national level. They have grown into multi-layered forests, providing peace and quiet in the city. The display and propagation greenhouses, each covering 350 m², have 500 taxa of flowering shrubs under glass. There are office buildings of more than 1000 m². The Herbarium houses over 1000 accessions of seed specimens and over 500 accessions of plant specimens.

More than 20 research programmes have been conducted in the Arboretum since its foundation; 8 scientific achievement prizes at ministerial or higher levels have been awarded. The major achievements include *Illustrated Woody Flora of Northeast China*; strains and the isolation technique of endomycorrhizal fungi of non-leguminous nitrogen-fixing trees; *Flora of China* vol. 20, part 2 (Salicaceae); preliminary report of phenological observations of major trees and shrubs in Shenyang; and the technique for cultivation of mushrooms on half-cooked sawdust medium. Four books and over 100 papers have been published.

The staff now totals 13, including 2 senior and 2 intermediate researchers and technicians.Seed exchange programmes and contacts are established with botanical gardens in 20 countries and regions. Foreign guests and Chinese professionals from universities, colleges and research institutions, as well as students, schoolchildren and tourists, come to visit the Arboretum.

The Arboretum focuses on scientific research while aiming at all-round development of garden construction, botanical and horticultural studies, public education and commercial utilization of plants, with emphasis placed on introduction and conservation of rare and endangered woody plants native to Northeast China and neighboring regions. Studies are continuing on nitrogen fixation of non-leguminous trees, physiological ecology of trees, urban forest ecology and environment protection. The Arboretum will become an ecological public park with natural scenery of forests, beautiful garden landscape and abundant scientific content, creating greater social, ecological and economic benefits.

Add: Shenyang Arboretum, Shenyang Institute of Applied Ecology, Chinese Academy of Sciences,

52 Wanliutang Lu, Shenyang, Liaoning 110015, China

Tel : (86-24) 4811558

Fax: (86-24) 3843313

Sorbus alnifolia.

The Temperate Woody Plants Section (Huicui Garden)

The Section occupies an area of 2 ha, with 293 taxa of woody plants belonging to 49 families introduced and cultivated. Specialized gardens for roses (*Rosa*), lilacs (*Syringa*), Spiraea (*Spiraea*), saxifrages (*Saxifraga*), honeysuckles (*Lonicera*) and maples (*Acer*) have been established.

Weigela florida, a flowering shrub.

A purple-flowered new cultivar of *Xanthoceras sorbifolia,* used for landscaping.

Spiraea trichocarpa, a shrub for ornament and honey.

Xanthoceras sorbifolia, a tree for seed oil, medicine and landscaping.

Acanthopanax sessiliflorus, a medicinal plant.

Acer triflorum, a small tree native to northeast and north China, is used for ornament and timber.

Sorbus alnifolia, a tree with ornamental fruits and wood good for making furniture.

Quercus mongolica, a timber tree distributed in north China.

Pterocarya stenoptera, a tree producing bark fibre for making rope and seed oil for industrial use.

Hydrangea bretschneideri, a garden shrub with large and pretty flowers in August and September.

Staghorn sumac (*Rhus typhina*) from North America is used for sand fixation and ornament.

Syringa dilatata, a lilac bearing large beautiful flowers early in the growing season , is a good shrub for ornament.

Syringa amurensis, a shrub for landscaping and honey.

Caragana frutex, a small ornamental shrub, also of medicinal use.

The Northeast China Endemic, Rare and Endangered Plants Section

Established in 1992, the Section now has over 60 species of rare and endangered woody plants introduced and cultivated, including 20 species under national protection.

Kalopanax septemlobus grows in broad-leaved forests and is a traditional medicinal plant, which also produces fine wood for furniture.

Taxus cuspidata, a rare species distributed in mixed forests of broad-leaved trees and *Pinus koraiensis*, contains the anticancer taxol. Due to its elegant shape the tree is also widely used for urban landscaping.

Rhodiola angusta is a perennial herbaceous plant under national protection. The whole plant is used medicinally as a tonic.

The Non-Leguminous Nitrogen-Fixing Trees Section

Established in 1992, the Section now has 15 nitrogen-fixing tree species belonging to 3 genera in its collection, which serves well the research programmes on resources of non-leguminous nitrogen-fixing tree species and on symbiotic nitrogen fixation. The trees include *Alnus glutinosa, A. japonica, Elaeagnus umbellata, E. angustifolia* and *Hippophae rhamnoides*.

The Gymnosperms Section

This Section, 1 ha in area, is under construction and has had 30 species of gymnosperms in cultivation. It will eventually hold 60−80 species and become a site for conservation of most of the gymnospermous plants of northeast China.

Alnus tinctoria.

Alnus glutinosa.

The snow-covered spruce (*Picea*) in winter.

Pinus tabulaeformis, an important timber tree for afforestation and landscaping in northern China, is handsome in shape and has been chosen as the city tree of Shenyang.

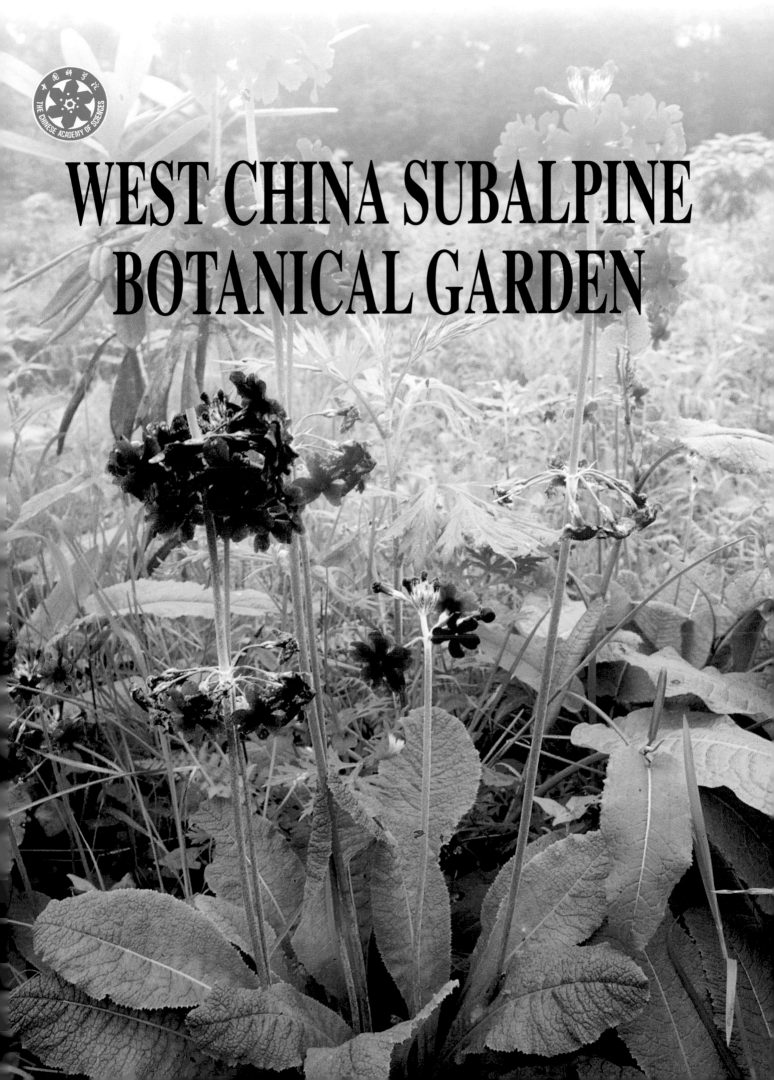

WEST CHINA SUBALPINE BOTANICAL GARDEN

Introduction

The West China Subalpine Botanical Garden is affiliated with the Institute of Botany, Chinese Academy of Sciences. It is located in Longchi, 30 km northwest of Dujiangyan City, Sichuan Province, in a transitional area between the West Sichuan Plain and the Qinghai-Tibet Plateau. The Garden site lies at lat. 30° 44′ N, long. 103° 27′ E, and 1400 – 3200 m altitude, with diverse landscapes and habitats of mountains, rivers, lakes, marshes, wetlands and screes. The climate has annual mean temperature of 8.5 – 10.9℃, extreme maximum temperature of 28℃, extreme minimum temperature of − 12℃, annual preciptation of 1800 mm and mean relative humidity of 87%. Native vascular plants amount to 2000 species, and all the vegetation types of the Hengduan Mountains are represented in the area. Some locally concentrated plant groups such as rhododendrons, mosses and ferns form the ready basis for construction of specialized gardens.

The Garden was jointly founded by the Institute of Botany of the Chinese Academy of Sciences and Dujiangyan City of Sichuan Province in 1986. It now occupies an area of over 100 ha, and has 8 regular staff members, including 3 senior and 3 junior researchers and technicians. Because of its special geographical position and successful construction policy, it has attracted great interests among botanists and horticulturists from home and abroad.

The Garden has a living collection of over 600 plant taxa, many of which are rare or endangered in the wild and have been propagated here. The Rhododendron Garden occupies a land area of 40 ha, conserving a collection of 40 000 plants of over 140 species of the genus. In addition, there are 3 natural communities of *Rhododendron* at different altitudes, with a total area of more than 60 ha. The Rhododendron Garden and the natural communities, together over 100 ha, form in area the largest base devoted to this group of plants by a single research institution in China. Other specialized gardens being planned or under construction include the Rare and Endangered Plants Garden, the Dove Tree *(Davidia involucrata)* Garden, the Primrose Garden, the Moss and Fern Garden and the Gymnosperms Garden. Special areas for biodiversity conservation research and for ecological monitoring and research will be constructed at 2000 – 3200 m altitudes.

In addition to its function as a botanical garden, it also has the character of a nature reserve. It will develop into a new-type botanical garden with the rich and unique floristic elements of the Qinghai-Tibet Plateau and the Hengduan Mountains contained in its natural setting and planted gardens.

Add: West China Subalpine Botanical Garden, Institute of Botany, Chinese Academy of Sciences,
    Dujiangyan City, Chengdu, Sichuan 611830, China
Tel : (86-28) 7283653
Fax: (86-10) 62590833

West China Subalpine Botanical Garden

Introduction

The West China Subalpine Botanical Garden is a new-type botanical garden that combines nature conservation, scientific research and tourism into one. Two bases, namely Xinguanshan and Longchi, have been established at 700−3200 m altitudes, where plants from subtropical evergreen broad-leaved forests as well as from temperate areas and high mountains can all be cultivated.

Gate of the Rhododendron Garden.

The Longxi River running through the Longchi base.

The Rhododendron Garden

Rhododendrons form a unique dominant feature of the Botanical Garden. Within the 40 ha of the Rhododendron Garden are conserved 40 000 plants of 200 Chinese *Rhododendron* species from Tibet, Yunnan, Sichuan and other parts of China and from the Royal Botanic Garden Edinburgh, UK. More rhododendrons that had been collected in China will be sent back from Edinburgh for cultivation and joint studies on their biodiversity.

Rhododendron.

Rhododendron vernicosum.

Rhododendron hunnewellianum, with large and showy inflorescences. It is endemic to western Sichuan.

Rhododendron calophytum, a native of the Garden.

Rhododendron specialist Dr D. Chamberlain investigates the growth of young plants of rhododendrons in the Garden.

West China Subalpine Botanical Garden

Rhododendron rex.

The Rare and Endangered Plants Garden

The floral elements of the Hengduan Mountains, Qinghai-Tibet Plateau and the rich collection of rare and endangered plants form another unique dominant feature of the Garden. The 5.3 ha land of the Rare and Endangered Plants Garden and the Dove Tree Garden is under construction, with nearly 70 species of rare and threatened plants being conserved here and many of them, including the dove tree (*Davidia involucrata*), being propagated in large numbers.

Dysosma veitchii under national protection.

Rhododendron rex, introduced from Liangshan Prefecture of Sichuan. A species under national protection.

Pinus roxburghii, under national protection.

The natural landscape of the Longchi base.

Primroses and Alpine Flowers

The Hengduan Mountains are an area rich in species of primroses (*Primula*). The Botanical Garden is therefore an ideal place for their introduction and cultivation. So far 40 primroses and many apline flowers have been collected and grown here.

Primula pycnoloba.

Lilium sargentiae.

Primula davidii, rediscovered in Sichuan in 1988, is listed as a nationally protected plant. Prior to its rediscovery, only 1 dried specimen was kept in the Museum in France.

Primula ovalifolia.

Cypripedium flavum and *Dysosma* sp.

Cypripedium flavum.

Primula pulverulenta has been multiplied in large numbers in the Garden. The tall, erect inflorescences bear large and showy pink flowers that last over 30 days.

Osmunda claytoniana with dimorphic fronds, of great ornamental value.